# PROBLEMS IN MATHEMATICAL PHYSICS
## with Solutions

# PROBLEMS IN MATHEMATICAL PHYSICS
## with Solutions

**I. V. MISYURKEYEV**

*translated by* Scripta Technica, Inc.

*editor of English edition*

Michael Yanowitch
*Department of Graduate Mathematics*
*Adelphi University*



**McGraw-Hill Book Company**

NEW YORK ST. LOUIS SAN FRANCISCO TORONTO LONDON SYDNEY

PROBLEMS IN MATHEMATICAL PHYSICS
with Solutions



*Library of Congress Catalog Card Number* 65-27785

Originally published as *Zadachi po Metodam Matematicheskoy Fiziki* by Moscow University Press, 1964.

1234567890 MR 721069876

# FOREWORD TO THE ENGLISH EDITION

This collection of problems and exercises is suitable for use in courses in which the student is expected to acquire some of the fundamental mathematical techniques for formulating and solving physical problems. In American universities, courses of this nature are usually given for advanced undergraduate and first year graduate students in various departments of physics, mathematics and engineering.

The first three chapters deal with basic properties of scalar and vector fields. The next three are devoted to the formulation of initial and boundary value problems, and to their solution by the method of waves, and the method of separation of variables. Chapter 6 includes material on special functions which is needed for the application of the method of separation of variables in polar and spherical coordinates. The last chapter contains problems on the theory of probability.

The abundance of hints, directions, and of completely worked out solutions make this little volume particularly valuable for self-study.

*M. Yanowitch*

*October, 1965*

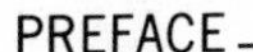

# PREFACE

This collection of problems and exercises in the methods of mathematical physics is designed to fit the present curriculum of the departments of physics and mathematics in universities and other institutes of higher education.

In compiling this collection, I made use of various text and problem books pertinent to the different sections.

To assist in the solution of the difficult problems, and to indicate more rational ways of solving them, I have given directions concerning methods of solution for most problems, and have included complete solutions of some. The more difficult problems are indicated by an asterisk.

The author considers it his pleasant duty to express his deep appreciation to Professor V. I. Levin, and also to Lecturers V. M. Rudyak and S. I. Mogilevskiy, who read the manuscript and made a number of valuable suggestions.

*I. V. Misyurkeyev*

# CONTENTS

# PART I

## The Foundations of Mathematical Field Theory

## CHAPTER 1

### *Two- and Three-Dimensional Scalar Fields*

### 1. Level curves and surfaces

**1.** Describe the level curves of the following functions $\varphi(x, y) = x^2 + y^2 - 1$; $\varphi(x, y) = \frac{x^2}{a^2} + \frac{y^2}{b^2} - 1$.

**2.** Construct the level curves of the following functions:
(a) $x - y$; (b) $e^x + x$; (c) $\sin x + \sin y$; (d) $\frac{1}{x^2 + y^2}$; (e) $\sqrt{xy}$;
(f) $\frac{1}{x^2}(2x - y + 1)$ $(x \neq 0)$.

**3.** Describe the level surfaces of the following fields:
(a) $\varphi = x + y + z$; (b) $\varphi = x^2 + y^2 + z^2$; (c) $\varphi = x^2 + y^2 - z^2$.

**4.** Describe the level surfaces of a plane-parallel field, of a field with axial symmetry, of a cylindrical field, and of a spherical field.

**5.** Describe the isothermal surfaces in the temperature field around a heated straight wire of infinite length.

**6.** What is the change in the temperature along an isotherm?

**7.** Describe the equipotential surfaces of the potential due to a point mass. Do the same for the potential due to a uniform mass distribution along a straight line segment.

**8.** Show that the level curves (resp. surfaces) do not pass through the extrema of a plane (resp. space) scalar field.

Can the level curves of the following plane fields pass through the points shown:
(a) $\varphi(x, y) = x^3 + y^3 - 3xy$ through $A(1, 1)$;
(b) $f(x, y) = 2xy - 3x^2 - 2y^2 + 10$ through $B(0, 0)$;
(c) $\psi(x, y) = 4(x - y) - x^2 - y^2$ through $C(2, -2)$?

**9.** A scalar $\varphi(x, y)$ is at every point $(x, y)$ equal to the sum of the distances of this point from two given fixed points $F_1$ and $F_2$ What are the level curves $\varphi = \text{const.}$?

**10.** In a three-dimensional space, $\varphi(M)$ is the sum of distances of a point $M$ from two fixed points. Find the level surfaces of the function $\varphi(M)$.

**11.** In a three-dimensional space, $\varphi(M)$ is the distance from the point $M$ to a fixed straight line. Find the level surfaces of the function $\varphi(M)$.

**12.** Consider two point charges $e_1$ and $-e_2$ at a certain distance from each other. Find the surface on which the potential $\varphi = \frac{e_1}{r_1} - \frac{e_2}{r_2}$ is equal to zero (where $r_i$ denotes the distance from the charge $e_i$ to an arbitrary point $P$ of the unknown surface).

## 2. Directional derivatives

**13.** Does the function $f(x, y) = 3x^4 - xy + y^3$ have a derivative in every direction at the point $M(1, 2)$?

**14.** Does the function $f(x, y) = \sqrt{xy + y^2 - 1}$ have a derivative in every direction at the point $M(0, 2)$?

**15.** Find the directional derivative of the function $5x^2 - 3x - y^2 - 1$ at the point $M(2, 1)$ along the line from this point to the point $N(5, 5)$.

**16.** Calculate the derivative of the function $f(x, y)$ in the following directions: (a) along the bisector of the first quadrant; (b) along the negative half of the $x$-axis.

**17.** Find the derivative of the field $y^2/x^2$ at a point on the ellipse $2x^2 + y^2 = C$ in the direction of the outward normal to the ellipse.

**18.** Find the magnitude of the derivative of the function $u = \ln(x^2 + y^2)$ at the point $M(x_0, y_0)$ in a direction perpendicular to the level curve passing through that point.

**19.** Find the magnitude of the derivative of the function $z = x^2 + y^2$ at the point $M(1, -2)$ in a direction perpendicular to the level curve passing through that point.

**20.** Show that the rates of increase of a field $\varphi$ at a given point in the direction of the normal $\mathbf{n}$ to the level surface passing through that point and in any other direction $\mathbf{l}$ are related by

$$\frac{\partial \varphi}{\partial l} = \frac{\partial \varphi}{\partial n} \cos(\mathbf{n}, \mathbf{l}).$$

From this, it follows (1) that the derivative in the direction $\mathbf{l}$ has its greatest value if this direction coincides with the direction of the normal $\mathbf{n}$ to the level surface and (2) that the derivative of the function in any direction tangent to the level surface is equal to zero.

**21.** In what direction should one take the derivative of the function $u = xy$ at the point $M_0(x_0, y_0)$ in order for the derivative to have its maximum value? What is the derivative of the given function in the direction tangential to the level curve $xy = x_0 y_0$ at the point $M_0(x_0, y_0)$?

## 3. The gradient of a function

**22.** Show that

$$\begin{aligned} &\operatorname{grad} Cu = C \operatorname{grad} u, \quad (C = \text{const.}), \\ &\operatorname{grad}(u + v) = \operatorname{grad} u + \operatorname{grad} v, \\ &\operatorname{grad}\left(\frac{u}{v}\right) = \frac{1}{v^2}(v \operatorname{grad} u - u \operatorname{grad} v), \\ &\operatorname{grad}(u^n) = n u^{n-1} \operatorname{grad} u, \\ &\operatorname{grad}[u(v)] = u'(v) \operatorname{grad} v. \end{aligned}$$

**23.** Show that

$$\operatorname{grad} f(\varphi, \psi) = \frac{\partial f}{\partial \varphi} \operatorname{grad} \varphi + \frac{\partial f}{\partial \psi} \operatorname{grad} \psi,$$

where $\varphi$ and $\psi$ are scalar fields possessing gradients and $f$ is a differentiable scalar function of its arguments.

**24.** Find the gradients of the following fields:
(a) $\varphi = 5x^2y - 3xy^5 + y^4z$; (b) $\varphi = x^3yz^2$; (c) $\varphi = e^{x+y+z}$; (d) $\varphi = y^2z - 2xyz + z^2$ at the point $M$ (0, 0, 0) and find the gradients of the fields (e) $\varphi = \arctan(y/x) + C$; (f) $\varphi = 1/r$ (where $r = \sqrt{x^2 + y^2 + z^2}$) at an arbitrary point other than the coordinate origin.

**25.** Find the derivative of the function $u = u(x, y, z)$ in the direction of the gradient of the function $v = v(x, y, z)$. Carry out the calculations in particular for the functions $u = x^2 + y^2 + z^2 - 1$ and $v = x + y + z$. Using these results, show that if grad $u$ is perpendicular to grad $v$, the derivative of the function $u$ in the direction of grad $v$ is zero.

**26.** Find the angle between the gradients of the field $\varphi = xy + yz + xz$ at the points $A$ (0, 1, 1) and $B$ (2, 0, 1).

**27.** Find the magnitude and direction of the gradient of the function $\varphi(x, y, z) = x^2 + 2y^2 + 3z^2 - xy - 4x + 2y - 4z$ at the point $M$ (0, 0, 0).

**28.** Find the gradient of the potential of the electric field caused by a point charge $e$ placed at the coordinate origin.

**29.** A temperature field is given by the function $T = x^2y - y^2z + 1$. What is the direction of the maximum temperature increase at the point $M_0$(0. 0, 1)?

**30.** At what points of the $xy$-plane is the gradient of the field $\varphi = x^2 + y^2 - 3xy$. (a) perpendicular to the $y$-axis; (b) parallel to the $y$-axis?

**31.** Figure 1 shows the vector $\mathbf{MN} = \text{grad } \varphi(x, y)$. Find by a geometrical construction the derivative of the scalar field $\varphi(x, y)$ in the directions **MA**, **MB**, and **MC** [where the direction of **MC** is tangent to the level curve $\varphi(x, y) = \varphi(M)$].

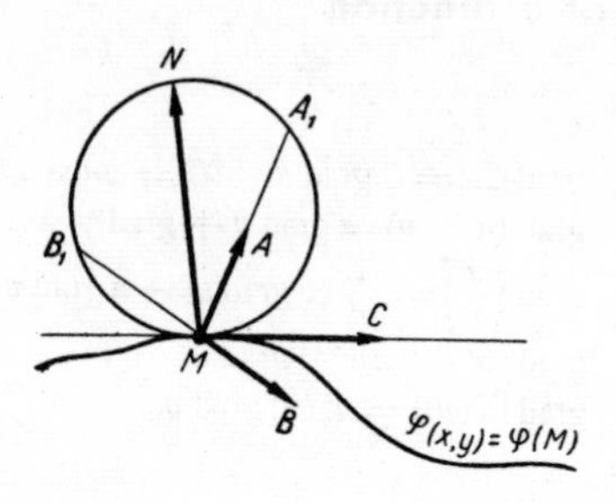


FIG. 1

**32.** A scalar field is given by the function $\varphi(x, y) = \frac{x^2}{a^2} + \frac{y^2}{b^2} - 1$. Show that at a point $M(x_0, y_0)$ on the level curve $\varphi(x, y) = 0$ the gradient of this field is equal to $\mathbf{r}^0 + \mathbf{R}^0$, where $\mathbf{r}^0$ and $\mathbf{R}^0$ are unit vectors in the directions $\mathbf{r} = \mathbf{F_1 M}$ and $\mathbf{R} = \mathbf{F_2 M}$ respectively, $F_1$ and $F_2$ being the foci of the ellipse serving as a level curve.

**33.** Consider an ellipsoid of revolution with foci at $P_1$ and $P_2$, and a mirrored inner surface. Suppose that a source of light is located at the point $P_1$. Show that all the rays of light originating at this focus and reflected from the surface of the ellipsoid will meet at the other focus $P_2$.

**34.** Suppose that the ellipsoid of the preceding problem is replaced with a paraboloid of revolution and that a source of light is located at its focus. Show that the rays of light originating at the focus will all be parallel after they are reflected from the paraboloid.

**35.** A scalar field is given by the function $\varphi = \varphi(r)$, where $r = \sqrt{x^2 + y^2 + z^2}$. Suppose, by treating $r$ as an arbitrary function of a parameter $\lambda$, we can represent $d\varphi$ in the form of the scalar product of some vector $\mathbf{g}$ (depending on $r$) and $d\mathbf{r}$:

$$d\varphi = \mathbf{g} \cdot d\mathbf{r},$$

Show that the vector $\mathbf{g}$ coincides with the vector grad $\varphi$.

Use this result to evaluate (a) grad $r$; (b) grad $r^2$; (c) grad $r^5$; (d) grad (ar) (where **a** is a constant vector); (e) $\int_C \text{grad}\, \varphi \cdot d\mathbf{r}$, where $\varphi = \varphi(x, y)$ is a differentiable function defined on a simply-connected domain $D$, $C$ is a closed curve in $D$, and **r** is the radius vector of the point $(x, y)$.

**36.** Calculate the gradients of the scalar fields

(a) $u = \begin{cases} \varphi_0 - \pi\rho r^2 \ (r \leqslant a), \\ \varphi_0 - \pi\rho a^2\left(1 + 2\ln\frac{r}{a}\right) \ (r \geqslant a) \end{cases}$; (b) $u = r + z\cos\theta$, expressed in terms of the cylindrical coordinates $r$, $\theta$, $z$ and of the fields (c) $u = -E_0 r\cos\theta\left(1 - \frac{R^3}{r^3}\right) + C$; (d) $u = 2\pi\rho\left(R^2 - \frac{r^2}{3}\right)$; (e) $u = \frac{qa^2}{r^3}(1 - 3\cos^2\theta)$; (f) $u = \mu\frac{\cos\theta}{r^2}$ expressed in terms of the spherical coordinates $r$, $\theta$, $\varphi$.

**37.** Suppose $(S)$ is a smooth curve (closed or otherwise) in the $xy$-plane and $\mu(P)$ is a continuous function defined on it. Then, the function

$$u(P_0) = \int_{(S)} \mu(P) \ln \frac{1}{r_{P_0P}}\, dS_P,$$

where $r_{P_0P}$ is the distance from an arbitrary point $P$ on the curve $(S)$ to a fixed point $P_0$ of the plane, is called the logarithmic potential of a simple layer and the function $\mu(P)$ is the density of this layer. Calculate the vector $\text{grad}_{P_0} u$ at a point $P_0$ not on the curve $(S)$.

**38*.** Suppose a continuous function $\mu(P)$ is defined in a bounded region $(\omega)$ of the $xy$-plane bounded by a piecewise-smooth closed curve $(\Gamma)$. Then, the function

$$v(P_0) = \iint_{(\omega)} \mu(P) \ln \frac{1}{r_{P_0P}}\, d\omega_P,$$

where $r_{P_0P}$ is the distance from an arbitrary point $P$ of the region $(\omega)$ to a fixed point $P_0$ of the plane is called the *logarithmic potential* of the region $(\omega)$ with density $\mu$. Find the vector $\text{grad}_{P_0} v$ at a point $P_0(x_0, y_0)$ lying outside the region $(\omega)$. Show that this representation of $\text{grad}_{P_0} v$ also holds when the point $P_0$ is in $(\omega)$.

Consider the behavior at infinity (as $r = \sqrt{x_0^2 + y_0^2} \to \infty$) of the logarithmic potential of a region and show that it can be represented in the form

$$v(P_0) = M \ln \frac{1}{r} + v^*(P_0),$$

where $v^*(P_0) \to 0$ as $r \to \infty$ and $r^2 |\mathrm{grad}_{P_0} v^*| < C$ ($C$ being some constant) and where $M = \iint_{(\omega)} \mu \, d\omega_P$ is the total "mass" in $(\omega)$.

**39*.** Let $(\Gamma)$ be a plane curve, $\varphi$-the angle between the normal to the curve $(\Gamma)$ at the point $P$ and the direction from this point to a fixed point $P_0(x_0, y_0)$, and $r_{P_0P}$-the distance between the points $P_0$ and $P$. Then, the expression

$$v(P_0) = \int_{(\Gamma)} \nu(P) \frac{\cos \varphi}{r_{P_0P}} \, dS_P,$$

is called the *logarithmic potential* of a double layer with dipole moment of density $\nu(P)$. Show that, for sufficiently large $r = \sqrt{x_0^2 + y_0^2}$

$$r^2 |\mathrm{grad}_{P_0} v| < C,$$

where $C$ is a positive constant.

## CHAPTER 2

# Vector Fields

### 1. Vector fields. Field lines

**40.** Show that, at a point $P(x, y, z)$, the gravitational field intensity $\mathbf{F}(P)$ due to a mass $m_0$ concentrated at a point $M_0(x_0, y_0, z_0)$ is equal to the gradient of the scalar field $\varphi(P) = -m_0/r$, where

$$r = r_{PM_0} = \sqrt{(x-x_0)^2 + (y-y_0)^2 + (z-z_0)^2}.$$

Generalize this result to the case of a Newtonian gravitational field caused by $n$ point masses $m_1, \ldots, m_n$.

**41.** Show that the gradient field of a plane-parallel scalar field is a plane-parallel vector field, that the gradient field of a scalar field with axial symmetry is also symmetric about the same axis, and that the gradient field of a spherical scalar field is a central vector field. Is the gravitational field of a point mass a central field?

**42.** Suppose that a unit mass is displaced along a given path $AB$ in a potential field. Show that the work done by a force $\mathbf{F}$ in causing this displacement is equal to the increase in the potential function $\varphi$ from the point A to the point B (the so-called *potential difference*).

**43.** Show that a central vector field $\mathrm{R} = \frac{f(r)}{r}\mathbf{r}$, where $f(r)$ is a scalar function of a positive argument, is derivable from a scalar potential. Find its potential.

**44.** Show that for a vector field to be derivable from a potential, it is necessary and sufficient that it be the gradient of some scalar field.

In problems 45-48, it is assumed that a unit mass is concentrated at the point in question and that on the attracting surfaces there is a uniform distribution of mass with unit density.

**45.** Find the force of attraction on a point $P(0, 0, \zeta)$ by a homogeneous surface of a sphere of radius $R$. Consider the cases $R > \zeta$, $R < \zeta$, $R = \zeta$.

**46.** With what force $\mathbf{F}$ does the homogeneous lateral surface of a right circular cylinder of altitude $h$ attract the center of the base of the cylinder?

**47.** Find the intensity of the field caused by the homogeneous lateral surface of a right circular cone of altitude $h$ at the center of the base.

**48.** Calculate the potential of a Newtonian attractive force at the point $P(0, 0, \zeta)$ by the homogeneous surface of a sphere or radius $R$. Consider the cases $R > \zeta$ and $R < \zeta$.

**49.** Compute the force with which a homogeneous sphere of radius $R$ and density $\mu$ attracts a material point of mass $m$ located at a distance $r$ (where $r > R$) from its center. Show that the force of interaction is the same as if the entire mass of the sphere were concentrated at its center.

**50.** Suppose there is a uniform mass (charge) distribution of density $\mu/2$ along a line segment of length $2l$ $(-l < z < l)$ which is parallel to the $z$-axis and does not pass through the point $P_0(x_0, y_0)$. Compute the potential and the field intensity $\mathbf{F}_l$ at $P_0(x_0, y_0)$ (see Fig. 2).

Solve this problem for the case in which the straight line is infinitely long (but still homogeneous).

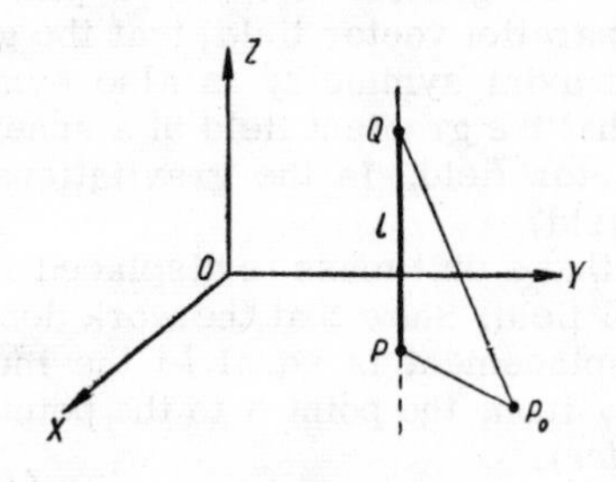


FIG. 2

**51.** A constant electric current $I$ flows upward along an infinitely long wire placed along the $z$-axis. Find the magnetic field intensity vector $\mathbf{H}$ and the lines of force, produced by the current, at an arbitrary point $M(x, y, z)$.

**52*.** Let $(v)$ denote a finite region in a three-dimensional space bounded by a piecewise-smooth closed surface $(S)$. Then, if a continous bounded function $\rho(P)$ is defined in $(v)$, the function

$$u(P_0) = \iiint\limits_{(v)} \rho(P) \frac{dv_P}{r_{P_0P}},$$

where $r_{P_0P}$ is the distance between a fixed point $P_0(x_0, y_0, z_0)$ of space and the point $P(x, y, z)$ of the region $(v)$, is called the *Newtonian potential* of the masses distributed in the region $(v)$ with density $\rho$ (or the Coulomb potential of spatially distributed charges).

(a) Calculate the vector $\text{grad}_{P_0} u$ at a point $P_0$ outside the region $(v)$.

(b) Show that if the point $P_0$ is sufficiently far away $r = \sqrt{x_0^2 + y_0^2 + z_0^2}$ from the coordinate origin, the following approximation holds:

$$u(P_0) \approx \frac{M}{r},$$

where $M = \iiint\limits_{(v)} \rho\, dv_P$ is the mass located in the region $(v)$.

(c) Examine the behavior of the potential $u(P_0)$ at infinity (that is, as $r \to \infty$). Show that in this case,

$$r^2 |\text{grad}_{P_0} u| < C,$$

where $C$ is a constant.

**53.** Find the field lines of the following vector fields.

(a) $x\mathbf{i} + 2y\mathbf{j}$; (b) $\mathbf{a} = (x^2 - y^2 - z^2)\mathbf{i} + 2xy\mathbf{j} + 2zx\mathbf{k}$; (c) $\mathbf{r} = x\mathbf{i} + y\mathbf{j} + z\mathbf{k}$; (d) $\mathbf{a} = x\mathbf{i} - y\mathbf{j} - 2z\mathbf{k}$; (e) the field $\mathbf{E} = q\mathbf{r}/r^3$ of a point charge $q$, where $r$ is the distance between the point in question and the charge.

**54.** Show that the field lines of the homogeneous field $\mathbf{R}$ (where $\mathbf{R}$ = const.) are parallel lines.

**55.** (a) Find the equation for the lines of force of the field of two parallel infinitely-long wires with charges of $+e$ and $-e$ per unit length.

(b) Find the equation for the lines of force of the electric field of a dipole at great distances from it in the $xy$-plane. Assume that the $y$-axis coincides with the direction of the dipole field vector $\mathbf{P}$.

**56.** Prove the following:

(a) If the vector field $\mathbf{a} = a_r\mathbf{e}_r + a_\varphi\mathbf{e}_\varphi + a_z\mathbf{e}_z$ is given in cylindrical coordinates (see Fig. 3a), the differential equations of the family of field lines of the field $\mathbf{a}$ are of the form

$$\frac{dr}{a_r} = \frac{r\, d\varphi}{a_\varphi} = \frac{dz}{a_z};$$

(b) If the vector field $\mathbf{a}=a_r\mathbf{e}_r+a_\theta\mathbf{e}_\theta+a_\varphi\mathbf{e}_\varphi$ is given in spherical coordinates (see Fig. 3b), the differential equations of the family of field lines of the field **a** are of the form

$$\frac{dr}{a_r}=\frac{r\sin\theta\,d\varphi}{a_\varphi}=\frac{r\,d\theta}{a_\theta}.$$

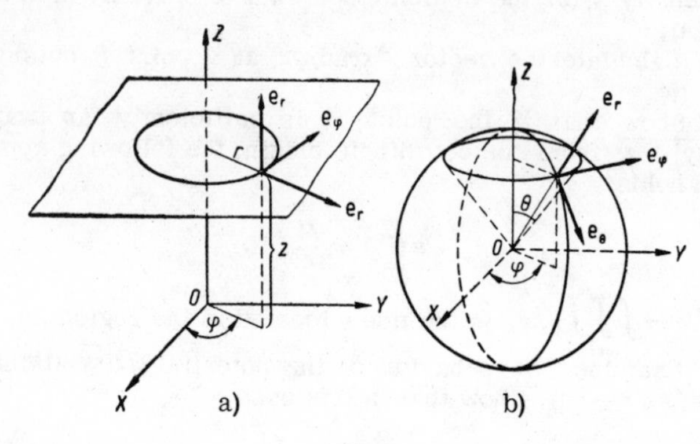


FIG. 3

**57.** Find the equation for the field lines of the field given in spherical coordinates by

$$\mathbf{a}=\frac{2a\cos\theta}{r^3}\,\mathbf{e}_r+\frac{a\sin\theta}{r^3}\,\mathbf{e}_\theta.$$

## 2. A hydrodynamical model

**58.** Let $\mathbf{v}=v_x\mathbf{i}+v_y\mathbf{j}$ be the velocity field corresponding to a steady potential flow of an ideal incompressible fluid. Show that the equation for the stream lines is $u(x, y)$ = const., where $u(x, y)$ is a stream function defined by the following line integral (to within an additive constant):

$$u(x, y)=\int_{(x_0,\, y_0)}^{(x,\, y)} v_x\,dy-v_y\,dx,$$

where $(x_0, y_0)$ is a fixed point, and $(x, y)$ a variable point in the field (which is assumed to be solenoidal, i.e., such that $\frac{\partial v_x}{\partial x}+\frac{\partial v_y}{\partial y}=0$ at all points of the field).

**59.** Let $\varphi=\varphi(x, y)$ be the potential of the velocity field $\mathbf{v}=v_x\mathbf{i}+v_y\mathbf{j}$ (solenoidal) of an incompressible fluid. Show that the stream function can be represented in the form:

$$u(x, y)=\int_{(x_0, y_0)}^{(x, y)} \frac{\partial \varphi}{\partial x} dy-\frac{\partial \varphi}{\partial y} dx+\text{const.},$$

where $(x_0, y_0)$ is a fixed point and $(x, y)$ is a variable point in the field.

**60.** Show that the potential $\varphi(x, y)$ and the stream function $u(x, y)$ corresponding to the velocity field $\mathbf{v}=v_x\mathbf{i}+v_y\mathbf{j}$ of a potential flow of an incompressible fluid are connected by means of the following partial differential equations (Euler-d'Alembert equations*):

$$\frac{\partial \varphi}{\partial x}=\frac{\partial u}{\partial y}, \quad \frac{\partial \varphi}{\partial y}=-\frac{\partial u}{\partial x}.$$

From this, deduce the following:

$$\varphi(x, y)=\int_{(x_0, y_0)}^{(x, y)} \frac{\partial u}{\partial y} dx-\frac{\partial u}{\partial x} dy+\text{const.}=$$

$$=\int_{(x_0, y_0)}^{(x, y)} v_x dx+v_y dy+\text{const.}$$

Show that the family of stream lines and the family of equipotential lines are mutually orthogonal.

**61.** Show that the velocity potential $\varphi(x, y)$ of the steady-state motion of an ideal incompressible liquid without sources or sinks, and also the stream function $u(x, y)$, satisfy Laplace's equation:

$$\frac{\partial^2 \varphi}{\partial x^2}+\frac{\partial^2 \varphi}{\partial y^2}=0, \quad \frac{\partial^2 u}{\partial x^2}+\frac{\partial^2 u}{\partial y^2}=0.$$

**62.** In the following problems, find the particle trajectories and the magnitude and direction of the velocity vector from the given velocity potential corresponding to the plane motion of an ideal incompressible liquid without sources or sinks:

(a) $\varphi=x$; (b) $\varphi=\frac{x}{x^2+y^2}$; (c) $\varphi=x+\frac{x}{x^2+y^2}$.

---

*More commonly called the Cauchy-Riemann equations.—Trans.

## 3. Surface integrals. The flux and divergence of a vector field. Ostrogradskiy's theorem*

**63.** Evaluate the surface integrals:

(1) $\iint\limits_S y\,dS$, where $S$ is the hemisphere $z = +\sqrt{R^2 - x^2 - y^2}$.

(2) $\iint\limits_S (x^2 + y^2)\,z\,dS$, where $S$ is the upper half of a sphere of radius $a$ with center at the coordinate origin.

(3) $\iint\limits_S z\,dS$, where $S$ is the total surface of the tetrahedron intercepted from the first octant by the plane $x + y + z = 1$.

(4) $\iint\limits_S \frac{z\,dS}{x^2 + y^2}$, where $S$ is that portion of the paraboloid $z = x^2 + y^2$ intercepted by the cylinder $x^2 + y^2 = a^2$.

(5) $\iint\limits_S x^2 y^2 z\,dx\,dy$, where $S$ is (a) the outer surface of the lower half of the sphere $x^2 + y^2 + z^2 = R^2$; (b) the inner surface of the same hemisphere.

(6) $\iint\limits_S z^2\,dx\,dy$, where $S$ is the outer surface of the ellipsoid $\frac{x^2}{a^2} + \frac{y^2}{b^2} + \frac{z^2}{c^2} = 1$.

(7) $\iint\limits_S xyz\,dx\,dy$, where $S$ is the outer surface of that portion of the sphere $x^2 + y^2 + z^2 = 1$ lying in the first and eighth octants: $x \geqslant 0$, $y \geqslant 0$.

(8) $\iint\limits_S (y - z)\,dy\,dz + (z - x)\,dx\,dz + (x - y)\,dx\,dy$, where $S$ is the upper side of the surface of the sphere $x^2 + y^2 + z^2 = 2Rx$ intercepted by the cylinder $x^2 + y^2 = 2rx$ (where $r < R$ and $z > 0$).

(9) $\iint\limits_S yz\,dx\,dy + xz\,dy\,dz + xy\,dx\,dz$, where $S$ is the outer side of the surface located in the first octant and formed by the cylinder $x^2 + y^2 = R^2$ and the plane $x = 0$, $y = 0$, $z = 0$, and $z = H$.

**64.** (a) Use Ostrogradskiy's formula to transform the surface integral

$$I = \iint\limits_S (x^2\,dy\,dz + y^2\,dx\,dz + z^2\,dx\,dy)$$

into an integral over the region $\omega$ bounded by the closed surface $S$.

(b) Use Ostrogradskiy's formula to evaluate the surface integral

$$\iint\limits_S (z^2 \cos(n,\ x) + x^2 \cos(n,\ y) + y^2 \cos(n,\ z))\,dS.$$

*More commonly called Gauss' or Green's theorem.—Trans.

(c) Set $Q=R=0$ and $P=uv$ in Ostrogradskiy's formula and obtain the formula for integrating a triple integral by parts:

$$\iiint\limits_{\omega} u\frac{\partial v}{\partial x}\,d\omega=-\iiint\limits_{\omega} v\frac{\partial u}{\partial x}\,d\omega+\iint\limits_{S} uv\cos(n,\,x)\,dS.$$

**65.** Suppose in a steady flow of an ideal incompressible fluid, the velocity of each particle is equal in magnitude and direction to the radius vector from the origin to the particle. How much fluid flows out of volume $T$ per unit time?

**66.** Find the flux of the vector $\mathbf{r}=x\mathbf{i}+y\mathbf{j}+z\mathbf{k}$ (a) through the outer side of the surface of a right circular cone whose apex coincides with the coordinate origin if the radius of the base of the cone is $R$ and its altitude is $H$; (b) through the outer side of the surface of a right circular cylinder whose lower base is centered at the coordinate origin (as with the cone, the radius of the base is $R$ and the altitude is $H$); (c) from a sphere of radius $R$ with center at the coordinate origin.

**67.** Calculate the flux of the vector $\mathbf{a}=(x-2y)\mathbf{i}+z\mathbf{j}+(3y+z)\mathbf{k}$ through that portion of the surface of a unit sphere with center at the coordinate origin that is contained in the first octant, that is, in the region in which $x^2+y^2+z^2>1$.

**68.** In a steady flow of an ideal incompressible liquid, the velocity of each particle is directed to the coordinate origin and has a magnitude equal to $1/r^2$, where $\mathbf{r}$ is the radius-vector of the particle. Calculate the amount of liquid flowing from a volume $G$ in unit time.

**69.** The projection of a certain vector $\mathbf{R}$ onto the outer normal of the surface of the tetrahedron formed by the planes $x+y+z=1$, $x\geqslant 0$, $y\geqslant 0$, $z\geqslant 0$ is equal to $1/(1+x+y)^2$. Calculate the outward flux of this vector through the surface.

**70.** The magnitude of a vector $\mathbf{R}$ at a given point $M$ is usually represented graphically by drawing field lines through a surface element $\Delta S$ that is perpendicular to the vector $\mathbf{R}$ at the point $M$. The number of lines drawn is proportional to the magnitude of the vector $\mathbf{R}$. Show that the flux of the field $\mathbf{R}$ through a surface $S$ is proportional to the number of field lines crossing the surface $S$.

**71.** (a) Calculate the flux of the electric field $\mathbf{E}=q\mathbf{r}/r^3$ due to a point charge $q$ across a sphere of radius $a$ with center at the charge. What is the flux if the charge $q$ lies outside the sphere? What is the flux of the vector $\mathbf{E}$ through an arbitrary surface?

(b) Show that the flux of an arbitrary field $\mathbf{R}$ through an arbitrary closed surface is equal to $4\pi$ times the sum of the masses $m_1, \ldots, m_n$ producing the field, that are enclosed by the surface:

$$Q(\mathbf{R};\ S) = -4\pi \sum_{k=1}^{n} m_k$$

(In electrostatics, this assertion is called the Gauss-Ostrogradskiy electrostatic theorem). The equation

$$Q(\mathbf{R};\ S) = -4\pi \iiint_{(v)} \mu(P)\, dv_P.$$

is a generalization of this assertion for the case of continuously distributed masses (or charges) with density $\mu(P)$ within the region $(v)$ bounded by a closed surface $S$.

**72.** A sphere of radius $a$ has an electric charge uniformly distributed over the surface with surface density $\sigma = q/4\pi a^2$. Find the intensity $\mathbf{D}$ of the field at points inside and outside the sphere.

**73.** An infinitely long circular cylinder of radius $a$ is electrically charged with a uniform surface density $\sigma$. Determine the intensity of the field at a point located at a distance $r$ from the axis of the cylinder. Consider the cases $r > a$ and $r < a$.

**74.** Suppose that a mass $m$ is concentrated at the coordinate origin. What is the flux of the gravitational field inward through the surface of a cylinder of radius $r$ and altitude $2h$ that is coaxial with the $z$-axis and has one base in the $xy$-plane?

**75.** An infinitely thin plane is electrically charged with a surface charge density $\sigma$. Find the intensity of the field at a point $M$ located at a distance $r$ from the plane.

**76.** Calculate the flux of the vector $\mathbf{a} = a_r\mathbf{e}_r + a_\varphi\mathbf{e}_\varphi + a_z\mathbf{e}_z$ (given in a cylindrical coordinate system) through that portion $S$ of a cylindrical surface of radius $r$ whose axis coincides with the $z$-axis.

**77.** Show that the flux of the vector $\mathbf{a} = a_r\mathbf{e}_r + a_\varphi\mathbf{e}_\varphi + a_\theta\mathbf{e}_\theta$ (given in a spherical coordinate system) through any portion $S$ of a spherical surface of radius $r$ with center at the coordinate origin is equal to the integral

$$\iint_S (\pm a_r)\, r^2 \sin\theta\, d\theta\, d\varphi.$$

**78.** Find the divergence of the field $\mathbf{R} = 5x\mathbf{i} + 3y\mathbf{j} - 2z\mathbf{k}$ and give a physical interpretation of this result.

**79.** What is the divergence of the homogeneous field $\mathbf{a} = a_x\mathbf{i} + a_y\mathbf{j} + a_z\mathbf{k}$ (where $a_x$, $a_y$, $a_z$ are constants)? Give a hydrodynamic interpretation of the result.

**80.** By using the definition of the divergence, evaluate

(a) the divergence of the vector $\mathbf{r}=x\mathbf{i}+y\mathbf{j}$ at the centers of the circle $x^2+y^2=R^2$ and of the square $-R\leqslant x, y\leqslant R$.

(b) the divergence of the field $\mathbf{r}=x\mathbf{i}+y\mathbf{j}+z\mathbf{k}$ at the center of the sphere $x^2+y^2+z^2=R^2$.

**81.** Does the field $\mathbf{R}=3x^2\mathbf{i}-5xy\mathbf{j}+z^2\mathbf{k}$ have either sources or sinks at the points $P_1(1, 2, 3)$, $P_2(1, -5, -1)$, $P_3(2, 0, -1)$? If so, determine their strength.

**82.** Evaluate the divergence of a central vector field $\mathbf{R}=f(r)\,\mathbf{r}$, where $f(r)$ is a differentiable function and $\mathbf{r}=x\mathbf{i}+y\mathbf{j}+z\mathbf{k}$, where $r=|\mathbf{r}|$.

**83.** Find the source distribution belonging to the vector field $\mathbf{R}=x\mathbf{i}-y^2\mathbf{j}+xz\mathbf{k}$ and the total output of the sources of the given field that lie within the sphere $x^2+y^2+z^2=1$.

**84.** Find the divergence of the velocity field $\mathbf{v}$ of a liquid rotating around an axis, and of the field $\mathbf{H}$ in problem 51.

**85.** A certain liquid that is moving with a velocity $\mathbf{v}$ fills a volume $G$. Assuming that the velocity field in the region $G$ is solenoidal, derive the equation of continuity:

$$\frac{\partial\rho}{\partial t}+\operatorname{div}(\rho\mathbf{v})=0,$$

where $\rho=\rho(x, y, z, t)$ is the density of the liquid at the instant $t$ at the point $(x, y, z)$.

From this, derive the condition for incompressibility of the liquid:

$$\operatorname{div}\mathbf{v}=0.$$

**86.** Experiment shows that the velocity of an incompressible liquid in a vector tube increases in places where the cross-section of the tube decreases. Explain this fact from the point of view of mathematical field theory.

Show that the fluxes of a solenoidal vector field through different cross sections of a vector tube are different.

**87.** (a) Show that the divergence of the gravitational field of a finite number of point masses is everywhere zero outside these masses. Generalize this assertion to the case of the gravitational field of a continuously distributed mass in a region $(v)$.

(b) Show that the divergence of the gravitational field $\mathbf{F}$ of a continuously distributed mass in a region $(v)$ is equal to

$$\operatorname{div}\mathbf{F}=-4\pi\mu,$$

where $\mu$ is the density of the substance.

**88.** The field of the electric displacement vector $\mathbf{D}$ is directed along the radius of a sphere $a$ and its values are given by

$$\mathbf{D}=\begin{cases} l\mathbf{r} & (0\leqslant r\leqslant a),\\ \dfrac{la^3}{r^3}\mathbf{r} & (a\leqslant r<\infty),\end{cases}$$

where $\mathbf{r}=x\mathbf{i}+y\mathbf{j}+z\mathbf{k}$, $r=|\mathbf{r}|$, and $0<l=$ const. Find the distribution of the charges producing this field.

**89.** Show that a central vector field $\mathbf{R}(r)=(f(r)/r)\,\mathbf{r}$ will be solenoidal only when the magnitudes of the vectors of this field are inversely proportional to the squares of the distances of the points in question from the center.

**90.** Evaluate the divergence of the following vectors:

(a) $\mathbf{a}=r^2z\mathbf{e}_r+z^2\varphi\mathbf{e}_\varphi-\frac{z^3}{3r}\mathbf{e}_z$, defined in cylindrical coordinates and

(b) $\mathbf{a}=a_r(r,\ \theta,\ \varphi)\,\mathbf{e}_r$; (c) $\mathbf{a}=\frac{2\cos\theta}{r^2}\mathbf{e}_r+\ \sin\ \theta\mathbf{e}_\theta$; (d) $\mathbf{a}=\frac{\cos\varphi}{r}\mathbf{e}_r+\varphi\mathbf{e}_\varphi-\frac{z}{r}\mathbf{e}_z$; (e) $-\nabla\left(\frac{\mu\cos\theta}{r^2}\right)$, defined in spherical coordinates.

**91.** Show that the fields $\mathbf{a}=y^2\mathbf{i}+z^2\mathbf{j}+x^2\mathbf{k}$ and $\mathbf{b}=\frac{2\cos\theta}{r^3}\mathbf{e}_r+\frac{\sin\theta}{r^3}\mathbf{e}_\theta$ (in spherical coordinates) are solenoidal.

## 4. The circulation of a vector field around a closed contour. The curl of a vector. Stokes' theorem

**92.** Calculate the circulation of the given vector field along the curve indicated and explain the physical meaning of the sign of the circulation (here and in what follows, we take the counterclockwise direction around a curve in a right-handed coordinate system as the positive direction);

(a) $\mathbf{a}=-y\mathbf{i}+x\mathbf{j}+5\mathbf{k}$, $(C)$: $x^2+y^2=1$, $z=0$;

(b) $\mathbf{a}=y\mathbf{i}+z\mathbf{j}+x\mathbf{k}$, $(C)$: the circle $x^2+y^2+z^2=a^2$, $x+y+z=0$;

(c) $\mathbf{a}=-\frac{y}{x^2+y^2}\mathbf{i}+\frac{x}{x^2+y^2}\mathbf{j}$, $(C)$: any simple closed curve (with no points of self-intersection);

(d) $\mathbf{a}=(x^3y+e^y)\,\mathbf{i}+(xy^3+xe^y-2y)\,\mathbf{j}$, $(C)$: any closed curve that is symmetric about the origin or about both coordinate axes;

(e) $\mathbf{a}=y\mathbf{i}-x\mathbf{j}$, $(C)$: the closed curve formed by the coordinate axes and the first quarter of the astroid $\mathbf{r}=R\cos^3t\cdot\mathbf{i}+R\sin^3t\cdot\mathbf{j}$;

(f) $\mathbf{a} = y^2\mathbf{i}$, $(C)$: the closed curve consisting of the right half of the ellipse $\mathbf{r} = a_1 \cos t \cdot \mathbf{i} + b_1 \sin t \cdot \mathbf{j}$ and a segment of the $y$-axis;

(g) $\mathbf{a} = (y-z)\mathbf{i} + (z-x)\mathbf{j} + (x-y)\mathbf{k}$, $(C)$: the circle $x^2+y^2+z^2 = R^2$, $y = x \tan \alpha$ (for $0 < \alpha < \pi$), where the positive direction is the counter-clockwise direction as viewed from the positive half $(x > R)$ of the $x$-axis;

(h) $\mathbf{R} = y^2z^2\mathbf{i} + x^2z^2\mathbf{j} + x^2y^2\mathbf{k}$ along the closed curve $x = a \cos t$, $y = a \cos 2t$, $z = a \cos 3t$, taken in the direction of increasing values of the parameter $t$.

**93.** (a) Show that the circulation of a vector field depends on its orientation in the field by calculating the circulation of the field $\mathbf{a} = y\mathbf{i}$ around the circle with center at the point $(0, b, 0)$ and radius $b$ that lies in the $xy$-plane and then for a circle of same radius and center that is located in the plane $y = b$.

(b) Calculate the curl of the field $\mathbf{a} = y\mathbf{i}$ around the circle $x = b \cos t$, $y = b + b \sin t$, $z = 0$ (for $0 \leqslant t \leqslant 2\pi$) at the center of this circle $P_0(0, b, 0)$ in the positive direction of the $z$-axis.

**94.** Calculate the circulation of the vector $\mathbf{H}$ in problem (51) around the circle $(L)$: $x^2 + y^2 = R^2$, $z = 0$. What is the circulation of this vector around any simple closed curve $(C)$ not encircling the conductor?

**95.** Suppose the components of the vector field $\mathbf{a} = a_x\mathbf{i} + a_y\mathbf{j} + a_z\mathbf{k}$ have continuous derivatives with respect to the coordinates in the neighborhood of a point $P$. Show that the curl of the field $\mathbf{a}$ at the point $P$ can be calculated from the formula

$$\operatorname{curl} \mathbf{a} = \nabla \times \mathbf{a} = \begin{vmatrix} \mathbf{i} & \mathbf{j} & \mathbf{k} \\ \frac{\partial}{\partial x} & \frac{\partial}{\partial y} & \frac{\partial}{\partial z} \\ a_x & a_y & a_z \end{vmatrix}.$$

From this formula, derive expressions for the components of the vector curl $\mathbf{a}$.

Use the formula given above to calculate the curl of the following vector fields at an arbitrary point:

(a) $\mathbf{R} = a\mathbf{i} + b\mathbf{j} + c\mathbf{k}$ (where $a$, $b$, and $c$ are constants),

(b) $\mathbf{R} = f(r)\,\mathbf{r}$, where $\mathbf{r} = x\mathbf{i} + y\mathbf{j} + z\mathbf{k}$, and $r = |\mathbf{r}|$.

**96.** Calculate the flux of the curl of the field $\mathbf{a} = x^3y^3\mathbf{i} + \mathbf{j} + z\mathbf{k}$: (a) through the hemisphere $z = +\sqrt{R^2 - x^2 - y^2}$, (b) through an arbitrary piecewise-smooth 2-sided surface $S$ "stretched" across the circle $x^2 + y^2 = R^2$, $z = 0$. Compare the two results. Show that the flux of the curl through a closed surface is independent of the shape of the surface and depends only on the shape and position of the curve bounding this surface.

**97.** A propeller of infinitely small radius with a large number of blades that can rotate freely about an axis is placed in the velocity field $\mathbf{v}$ of a liquid in motion. Let $\mathbf{l}$ denote a unit vector in the direction of the axis of the propeller. Show that the magnitude of the angular velocity $\omega$ of the propeller will be greatest if the vector $\mathbf{l}$ is directed along the vector curl $\mathbf{v}$. Show that the angular velocity vanishes if the axis of rotation is perpendicular to the direction of the vector curl $\mathbf{v}$. Finally, show that it is neither zero nor its maximum value if the axis of rotation is in any other direction.

**98.** Show that Stokes' formula can be written in vector form as follows:

$$\int_L \mathbf{F}\, d\mathbf{L} = \iint_S \text{curl}\, \mathbf{F}\, d\mathbf{S},$$

where $d\mathbf{L} = dL\boldsymbol{\tau}$, $d\mathbf{S} = \mathbf{n}\, dS$, $\boldsymbol{\tau}$ is a unit vector tangential to the curve $L$ in the positive direction, and that $\mathbf{n}$ is a unit vector normal to the surface $S$.

**99.** Show that the direction of the curl of the velocity field corresponding to the flow of a liquid rotating like a solid around some axis is along the axis of rotation and that its magnitude is equal to twice the angular velocity.

**100.** Show that the circulation of the magnetic field intensity $\mathbf{H}$, due to an electric current, around a closed curve is equal to $4\pi/c$ times the albegraic sum of the currents "threading" the curve, where $c$ is the velocity of light in a vacuum.

**101.** Calculate the curl of the field $\mathbf{R}(P) = f(\rho)\, \boldsymbol{\tau}(P)$, where $\rho$ is the distance from the point $P$ to a fixed straight line $l$ and $\boldsymbol{\tau}(P)$ is a unit vector perpendicular both to the line $l$ and to the line drawn from the point $P$ to the line $l$ (see Fig. 4). Assume that the function $f(\rho)$ is differentiable.

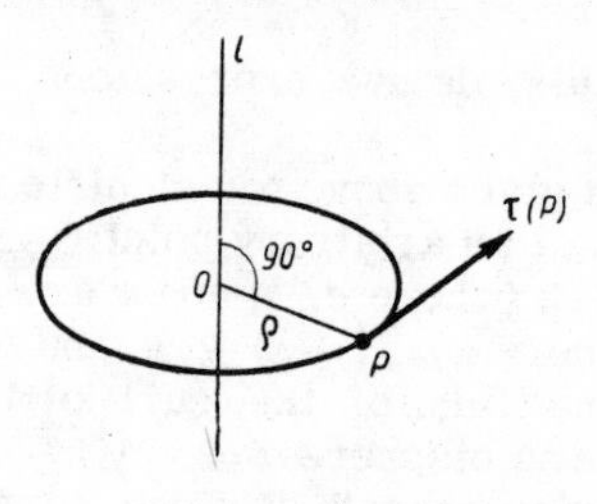


FIG. 4

**102.** Find conditions which are necessary and sufficient for the field of the preceding problem to be irrotational.

**103.** Show that the circulation of the magnetic field intensity $\mathbf{H}$, due to an electric current, around a closed curve $l$ that does not encircle any current-carrying conductor is equal to zero. Compare this result with the assertion in problem 100.

**104.** Determine the *angular* velocity $\boldsymbol{\omega}$ with which a rigid body rotates about an axis that passes through some point of the body if its *linear* velocity is given by $\mathbf{v} = 2x\mathbf{i} + y^2\mathbf{j} + xz\mathbf{k}$.

**105.** Show that the field of the curl of a vector $\mathbf{R}$ is free of sources.

**106.** Show that the flux of the curl of a vector $\mathbf{R}$ through an arbitrary closed surface $S$ is zero.

**107.** Calculate the total strength of sources of the field of the curl of a vector $\mathbf{R}$ that are enclosed by a closed surface $S$.

**108.** The velocity of each particle of a liquid in plane steady flow is characterized by the vector

$$\mathbf{V} = u\mathbf{i} + v\mathbf{j}.$$

(1) Find the amount of the liquid $Q$ that flows through a closed contour $C$ enclosing a region $S$ containing the source of the liquid. (2) Calculate the circulation $\Gamma$ of the velocity vector $\mathbf{V}$ around the curve $C$. (3) Show that the components $u$ and $v$ of the field $\mathbf{V}$ satisfy the Euler-d'Alembert (or Cauchy-Riemann) equations

$$\frac{\partial u}{\partial x} = \frac{\partial v}{\partial y}, \quad \frac{\partial u}{\partial y} = -\frac{\partial v}{\partial x},$$

if the liquid is incompressible and the flow is irrotational.

**109.** In a source-free space, a magnetic field $\mathbf{H}$ satisfies the equations

$$\operatorname{curl} \mathbf{H} = 0, \quad \operatorname{div} \mathbf{H} = 0.$$

Show that these equations imply that

$$\mathbf{H} = -\operatorname{grad} u, \quad \Delta u \equiv \frac{\partial^2 u}{\partial x^2} + \frac{\partial^2 u}{\partial y^2} + \frac{\partial^2 u}{\partial z^2} = 0,$$

where $u$ is the potential of the field $\mathbf{H}$.

**110.** Suppose that a direct current $I$ is flowing through a cylindrical wire of radius $a$. Find the magnetic field intensity at an arbitrary point located at a distance $r$ from the wire.

**111.** Find the magnetic field intensity caused by a direct current $I$ flowing down a hollow cylindrical tube.

**112.** Derive the differential equations of the magnetic field of a direct current:

$$\operatorname{curl} \mathbf{H} = \frac{4\pi}{c} \mathbf{j}, \tag{1}$$

$$\operatorname{div} \mu \mathbf{H} = 0, \tag{2}$$

where $\mathbf{j}$ is the current-density vector, $\mu$ is the magnetic permeability of the medium, and $c$ is the velocity of light in a vacuum.

**113.** Prove (a) that every field derivable from a scalar potential is an irrotational field and (b) that identical vanishing of the curl of a differentiable vector field in a simply-connected domain implies that the field is derivable from a scalar potential.

**114.** Show that the fields $\mathbf{a} = x^3\mathbf{i} - y^3\mathbf{j} + z^3\mathbf{k}$ and $\mathbf{b} = yz(2x + y + z)\mathbf{i} + xz(x + 2y + z)\mathbf{j} + xy(x + y + 2z)\mathbf{k}$ and the magnetic field $\mathbf{H}$ of the line current $I$ in problem 51 have corresponding potentials and evaluate their potentials. How can we reconcile the statement that the field $\mathbf{H}$ has a potential with the answer to problem 94?

**115.** Calculate the curl of the following fields:

(a) The axis-symmetric fields $\mathbf{a} = a_r(r, z)\mathbf{e}_r + a_z(r, z)\mathbf{e}_z$ and $\mathbf{b} = r^2 z\mathbf{e}_r - rz^2\mathbf{e}_z$;

(b) a central field $\mathbf{a} = a_r(r, \theta, \varphi)\mathbf{e}_r$; and fields:

(c) $\mathbf{a} = \sin\varphi\mathbf{e}_r + \frac{\cos\varphi}{r}\mathbf{e}_\varphi - rz\mathbf{e}_z$;

(d) $\mathbf{a} = \frac{\cos\theta}{r^3}\mathbf{e}_r + \frac{\sin\theta}{r^3}\mathbf{e}_\theta$;

(e) $\mathbf{a} = \frac{2\mu\cos\theta}{r^3}\bar{\mathbf{e}}_r + \frac{\mu\sin\theta}{r^3}\mathbf{e}_\theta$.

# CHAPTER 3

## *Second-Order Differential Operators. The Laplacian. Harmonic Functions*

**116.** Show that

$$\operatorname{div}(\psi \operatorname{grad} \varphi) = \psi \nabla^2 \varphi + \nabla \varphi \cdot \nabla \psi$$

and

$$\Delta(\varphi\psi) = \varphi\, \Delta\psi + \psi\, \Delta\varphi + 2\nabla\varphi \cdot \nabla\psi.$$

**117.** Calculate the Laplacian of the functions $2\mu \ln (1/r)$ (where $r^2 = x^2 + y^2$ and $\mu$ = const.), $(1/r)$ (where $r^2 = x^2 + y^2 + z^2$) and

$$r\frac{\partial u}{\partial r}, \quad \frac{1}{r}\frac{\partial (r^2 u)}{\partial r} \; (r^2 = x^2 + y^2 + z^2),$$

In the last two expressions, assume that $u = u(x, y, z)$ is harmonic.

**118.** It is shown in electrodynamics that the intensity **E** of an electric field caused by a charge density $\rho$ satisfies Maxwell's equations for an electrostatic field at every point of the region in question:

$$\operatorname{div} \mathbf{E} = \frac{4\pi}{\varepsilon}\rho, \quad \operatorname{curl} \mathbf{E} = 0.$$

Find the field **E**.

**119.** Suppose that the divergence and the curl of some field **a** are given at all points of a region $(v)$ bounded by a surface $S$:

$$\operatorname{curl} \mathbf{a} = \mathbf{b}, \quad \operatorname{div} \mathbf{a} = c, \tag{1}$$

and that the values of the normal component $a_n$ of the vector **a** on the boundary $S$ are given:

$$a_n = f(S). \tag{2}$$

Show that there exists a unique vector **a** satisfying equations (1) and the boundary condition (2).

**120.** Show that if a function $u(x, y, z)$ is harmonic in a region $(\omega)$ bounded by a surface $(S)$, then

$$\iiint_{(\omega)} |\nabla u|^2 \, d\omega = \iint_{(S)} u \frac{\partial u}{\partial n} dS.$$

**121.** By using the expressions for the Laplacian in cylindrical and spherical coordinates, find the general form of the function $u = u(r)$ such that $\Delta u = 0$.

**122.** Write Ostrogradskiy's formula for the vector grad $\varphi$. By using this relation, show that, if $\varphi$ is a harmonic function in a region $T$ bounded by a surface $S$, then

$$\iint_S \frac{\partial \varphi}{\partial n} dS = 0.$$

Give a hydrodynamic interpretation of this result by considering the flux of the velocities $\mathbf{v} =$ grad $\varphi$ of the steady motion of a liquid.

**123.** Show that if the functions $\varphi$ and $\psi$ are harmonic inside the surface $S$, then

$$\iint_S \varphi \frac{\partial \psi}{\partial n} dS = \iint_S \psi \frac{\partial \varphi}{\partial n} dS.$$

**124.** Show that if a nonconstant function $u(x, y, z)$ is harmonic and continuous in a region it cannot have extreme values in the interior of the region but attains them only on its boundary (the maximum-minimum principle).

Use this theorem to show that if two harmonic functions $u_1$ and $u_2$ coincide on the boundary of a region, they must also coincide everywhere within that region.

**125.** Can a vector field with nonzero divergence possess a vector potential?

**126.** Evaluate the magnetic field of an infinitely long straight wire conducting a current $I$ by evaluating first the vector potential **A** and then the field intensity from the formula **H** = curl **A**.

**127.** Calculate the vector potential of a system of currents flowing in three mutually orthogonal infinitely long conductors at a point $P(x, y, z)$ as shown in Fig. 5.

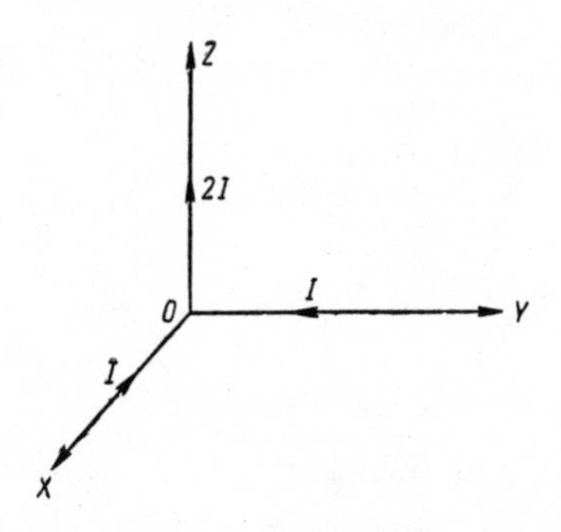


FIG. 5

**128.** The vector potential of the magnetic field of a circular current $I$ with radius $a$ is, at great distances $R$ (that is, $R \gg a$),

$$\mathbf{A} = \frac{1}{R^3} [\boldsymbol{\mu}, \mathbf{R}],$$

where $\boldsymbol{\mu}$ is the magnetic moment of the current. Evaluate the intensity of the field $\mathbf{H}$.

**129.** Calculate the potential $u$ of the electrostatic field caused by a sphere of radius $R$ throughout which a charge $e$ is uniformly distributed.

**130.** By integrating Laplace's equation in spherical coordinates, calculate the potential of an electrostatic field inside and outside a conducting sphere of radius $a$ on the surface of which a charge $e$ is uniformly distributed.

**131.** Calculate the potential and intensity of the field of an infinite circular cylinder of radius $a$ if its interior is electrically charged with a uniform density $\rho$.

# PART II

## Differential Equations of Mathematical Physics

CHAPTER 4

# Solution of the Vibrating String Equation by the Method of Waves (d' Alembert's Method)

**132.** Suppose the vibrations of an infinitely long string are excited by an initial displacement of the segment $(-C, C)$ in the shape of a parabola, symmetric with respect to the $u$-axis ($u$ denotes the displacement from equilibrium).

Formulate the initial value problem under the assumption that the string is initially at rest, and that the maximum initial displacement is $h$.

**133.** Formulate the mixed initial-boundary value problem for the longitudinal oscillations of a rod of uniform cross section, under the hypothesis that one end ($x = 0$) is rigidly fastened, while the other end ($x = l$) is free, and that the initial displacement and velocity are respectively $\mu(x)$and $\nu(x)$.

**134.** Derive the equation for small torsional vibrations of a homogeneous cylindrical rod of length $l$. Give a mathematical formulation of the problem of torsional vibrations of a rod with one end clamped and a pulley fastened to the other end.

**135.** Solve the Cauchy problems

$$\text{(a)}\quad \left.\begin{aligned} &\frac{\partial^2 u}{\partial t^2} = \frac{\partial^2 u}{\partial x^2}, \\ &u(x, 0) = \sin x, \quad \frac{\partial u(x, 0)}{\partial t} = 0 \end{aligned}\right\} \quad (-\infty < x < \infty, \ t > 0)$$

$$\text{(b)}\quad \left.\begin{aligned} &\frac{\partial^2 u}{\partial t^2} = a^2 \frac{\partial^2 u}{\partial x^2}, \\ &u(x, 0) = 0, \quad \frac{\partial u(x, 0)}{\partial t} = A \sin x \ (A = \text{const.}) \\ &(-\infty < x < \infty, \ t > 0). \end{aligned}\right\}$$

**136.** Suppose that a homogeneous infinitely-long string, satisfying the initial conditions

$$u(x, 0) = \mu(x), \quad \frac{\partial u(x, 0)}{\partial t} = \nu(x) \quad (-\infty < x < \infty)$$

is subjected to a uniform external load distribution $q(x, t)$. Find the displacement of an arbitrary point on the string for $t > 0$.

**137.** Find the distribution of voltages and currents along an infinitely long conducting wire possessing self-inductance $L$, capacitance $C$, resistance $R$, and leakage $G$, all measured per unit of length, assuming that the initial conditions are

$$v(x, 0) = \varphi(x), \quad I(x, 0) = \psi(x) \qquad (-\infty < x < \infty),$$

and that the four parameters listed are related by the equation $R/L = G/C$ (distortionless line).

**138.** Suppose that at an initial instant of time, a semi-infinite string $0 \leqslant x < \infty$ has the following shape

$$u = \begin{cases} 0 & \text{for } x \leqslant C, \\ \frac{h}{C}(x - C) & \text{for } C \leqslant x \leqslant 2C, \\ -\frac{h}{C}(x - 3C) & \text{for } 2C \leqslant x \leqslant 3C, \\ 0 & \text{for } x \geqslant 3C \end{cases} \qquad (h > 0, \ C > 0)$$

Draw the profiles of the string corresponding to the instants $t_1 = C/a$, $t_2 = 2C/a$, $t_3 = 3C/a$, and $t_4 = 7C/2a$ (where $a$ is the velocity of propagation along the string).

**139.** Solve the equation

$$u_{tt} = a^2 u_{xx}, \qquad (0 < x < \infty, \ t > 0)$$

with boundary and initial conditions

$$u(x, 0) = \mu(x), \quad \frac{\partial u(x, 0)}{\partial t} = \nu(x);$$
$$u(0, t) = \psi(t).$$

Calculate the solution when $\mu(x) = x^2$, $\nu(x) = \sin x$, and $\psi(t) = t$.

**140.** Suppose a backward wave described by $f(x, t) = 1/2 \sin \pi(x + t)$ was traveling along a semi-infinite string $0 < x < \infty$ with velocity $a = 1$ when $t < 0$. Calculate the displacement from equilibrium of the point $x = 2\pi$ at the time $t = 10$ sec (a) if the end $x = 0$ is fixed, (b) if the end $x = 0$ is free ($u_x(0, t) = 0$).

**141.** The end $x=0$ of a semi-infinite rod $0 \leqslant x < \infty$ moves according to the law $u(0, t) = Ae^{-Kt}$ beginning at $t=0$. Here, $A$ and $K$ are constants. Find the displacement $u(x, t)$ of points of the rod for $t > 0$ if the initial velocities and displacements are equal to zero.

**142.** The end $x=0$ of a semi-infinite string whose cross section is a circle of diameter 1 mm undergoes a harmonic transverse vibration of the form $A \cos \omega t$ (where $A = \text{const.}$). Find the displacement $u(x, t)$ of the string at an arbitrary instant of time and also the velocity of propagation of a wave if the tension is $T = 4$ kg and the density is 7.8 gm/cm$^3$. Assume that the initial displacement and initial velocity of points on the string are both zero.

**143.** A semi-infinite tube $0 < x < \infty$ filled with an ideal gas has a freely moving piston of mass $M$ at the end of $x=0$. At the instant $t=0$, a blow imparts to the piston an initial velocity $v_0$. Study the propagation of a wave in the gas if the initial displacements and velocities of particles of the gas are both zero.

**144.** A semi-infinite string $x \geqslant 0$ of linear density $\rho$ and tension $\rho a^2$ is originally in a state of rest. For $t > 0$, the point $x=0$ undergoes small vibrations given by $A \sin \omega t$. Find the displacement of an aribtrary point $x$ of the string.

**145.** At the end $x=0$ of a semi-infinite cylindrical tube filled with gas, a piston executes harmonic oscillations with displacement $A \sin \omega t$. At some initial instant of time, the condensation and the particle velocities are zero. Determine the displacement $u(x, t)$ of the gas for $t > 0$.

**146.** Suppose the initial shape of a homogeneous string whose ends at $x=0$ and $x=l$ (see Fig. 6) are fixed is that of a parabola symmetric with respect to the perpendicular line drawn

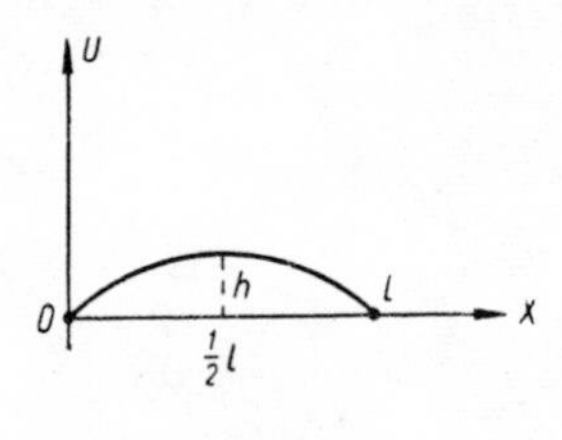


FIG. 6

through the point $x = l/2$. Suppose that its maximum displacement is $h$. Determine graphically the displacement of the string at the instants $t_1 = l/2a$ and $t_2 = l/a$, where $a$ is the velocity of propagation, assuming that the string is initially at rest.

**147.** Solve the following boundary-value problem:

$$\left.\begin{aligned} &u_{tt} = a^2 u_{xx}, \\ &u(x, 0) = \mu(x), \quad u_t(x, 0) = \nu(x), \\ &\qquad u(0, t) = u(l, t) = 0 \end{aligned}\right\} \quad (0 < x < l,\ t > 0)$$

**148.** Suppose a gas is initially at rest, and that the initial condensation $S_0$ is constant inside a sphere of radius $R$, and vanishes outside the sphere. Determine the condensation $S$ for all $t > 0$ outside of the region where the gas is initially disturbed.

**149.** Find the displacement for $t > 0$ of points on a finite homogeneous string which is initially at rest, if the end points $x = 0$ and $x = l$ are fixed, while the initial velocities are zero and the initial displacement is given by

$$u(x, 0) = A \sin \frac{\pi x}{l} \quad \text{for} \quad 0 \leqslant x \leqslant l$$

ƆHAPTER 5

# The Fourier Method. The Method of Eigenfunctions

## 1. Problems associated with the one-dimensional wave equation

**150.** Find the natural frequencies of the transverse vibra-ions of a string of length $l$, linear density $\rho$, and tension $T$ that s fastened at both ends.

**151.** Find the natural frequencies of the longitudinal vibra-ions of a rod $0 \leqslant x \leqslant l$, the left end of which is fastened, if a force $F(t) = At$ (where $A$ = const.) is applied to the right end at the nstant $t = 0$. Assume that the medium offers no resistance to he vibrations.

Solve this problem with the hypothesis that a weight of mass $M_0$ is attached to the free end.

**152.** Find the frequency of vibrations of a string 10 cm long vith rectangular cross section, 0.2 mm × 0.4 mm if its density s $\gamma = 7.8$ gm/cm$^3$ and if the tension in it is 1 kg.

**153.** One end of a rod $(0 \leqslant x \leqslant l)$ is fastened $(x = 0)$ and the other is free. What are the amplitude and the period of the free oscillations of the rod if the initial conditions are of the form

$$\varphi(x, 0) = \mu(x), \quad \varphi_t(x, 0) = \nu(x)$$

**154.** Find the law of vibration of a homogeneous string of ength $l$ with both ends fixed if at the initial instant it has the shape of a parabola symmetric with respect to a line perpendic-ılar to the string at its midpoint. The string is initially at rest.

Solve this problem under the assumption that the length of he string is $l = \pi$ and that the initial deviation from the equi-ibrium position is given by $\mu(x) = \sin x$.

**155.** Integrate the equation of small longitudinal vibration of a cylindrical rod of length $l$ one end of which ($x=0$) is fastene and the other is free. The initial displacement and velocity ar respectively $\mu(x)$ and $\nu(x)$. Apply the general formula to the cas in which $\mu(x)=x^2$ and $\nu(x)=\sin x$.

**156.** Suppose that a homogeneous string with fixed end $x=0$ and $x=l$ is stretched by displacing the point $x=x_0$ a dis tance $h$ from the equilibrium position and released with zer initial velocity at the instant $t=0$. Calculate the energy of th $n$th harmonic of the vibrating string.

**157.** Examine the forced vibrations of a string of finit length ($0\leqslant x\leqslant l$) caused by a periodic disturbing force $q=A\sin\omega t$ under the hypothesis that the ends of the string ar fastened and the initial conditions are nonhomogeneous:

$$u(x,\ 0)=\mu(x),\quad u_t(x,\ 0)=\nu(x)$$

where $\mu(x)$ and $\nu(x)$ are given continuous functions defined fo $0\leqslant x\leqslant l$ that vanish at $x=0$ and $x=l$ (compatibility conditions) Do not consider the resonant case.

**158.** Show that the solution of the equation

$$u_{tt}=u_{xx}+t^k$$

for $x\in[0,\ \pi]$ and $t>0$ that satisfies the conditions

$$u(0,\ t)=u(\pi,\ t)=0,$$
$$u(x,\ 0)=u_t(x,\ 0)=0,$$

is the function

$$u(x,\ t)=\frac{4}{\pi}\sum_{n=1}^{\infty}\frac{\sin nx}{n^2}\int_0^t\tau^k\sin n(t-\tau)\,d\tau$$

where $k$ is an arbitrary natural number.

**159.** A homogeneous rod of length $2l$, with center at th point $x=0$, is compressed by forces applied to its ends. Thi compression shortens the rod to a length $2l(l-\varepsilon)$. At the in stant $t=0$, these forces are removed. Find the displacemen $u(x,\ t)$ of a cross section with abscissa $x$ for $t>0$.

**160.** A string with fixed ends is set into vibration by a blov from a flat hammer which imparts to it the following initia velocity distribution:

$$u_t(x,\ 0)=\nu(x)=\begin{cases}0 & 0\leqslant x\leqslant x_0-\delta,\\ v_0 & x_0-\delta\leqslant x\leqslant x_0+\delta,\\ 0 & x_0+\delta\leqslant x\leqslant l.\end{cases}$$

Find the vibrations of the string if the initial displacement is 0. Solve the problem under the condition that the string is set into vibration by a *sharp* hammer which gives it an inpulse $P$ at the point $x_0$.

**161.** A string fastened at the end points is displaced by a force $F_0$ applied at the point $x=c$. Find the vibrations of the string if this force is suddenly removed at the initial instant.

**162.** One end of a rod is held in place and a constant force $F_0$ is applied to the other. Find the longitudinal vibrations of the rod if this force is removed at the initial instant.

**163.** A string of length $l$ is placed in a medium that offers a resistance proportional to the speed of motion of the string. In this case, the wave equation has the form

$$\frac{\partial^2 u}{\partial t^2} = a^2 \frac{\partial^2 u}{\partial x^2} - 2k \frac{\partial u}{\partial t}$$

where $k = h/\rho$ ($h$ being a proportionality constant and $\rho$ the density of the string).

Solve this equation by the Fourier method with the initial conditions

$$u(x, 0) = f(x), \quad \frac{\partial u(x, 0)}{\partial t} = F(x)$$

and the boundary conditions

$$u(0, t) = u(l, t) = 0$$

**164.** A continuously distributed force with linear density $x \sin \omega t$ is suddenly applied to a string fastened at the ends. Find the purely forced vibrations of the string. Neglect the resistance.

**165.** Find the general solution of the problem of transverse vibrations of a beam simply supported at its end $x=0$ and $x=l$ subject to arbitrary initial conditions:

$$u(x, 0) = f(x), \quad \frac{\partial u(x, 0)}{\partial t} = g(x) \quad (0 < x < l)$$

**166.** An isolated homogeneous electric cable $0 \leqslant x \leqslant l$ is charged to some constant potential. At the initial instant, the end $x=0$ is grounded, while the end $x=l$ remains isolated. Find the potential distribution in the conductor if the self-inductance is $L$, the resistance is $R$ and the capacitance is $C$ per unit length of the conductor.

**167*.** In the region $Q\begin{pmatrix}0\leqslant x\leqslant l\\0\leqslant t\leqslant\infty\end{pmatrix}$, the following mixed boundary-value problem is posed:

$$\rho(x)\frac{\partial^2 u}{\partial t^2}=L(u),$$

$$u(0,\ t)=u(l,\ t)=0,\quad u(x,\ 0)=\mu(x),\quad \frac{\partial u(x,\ 0)}{\partial t}=\nu(x).$$

where

$$L(u)=\frac{\partial}{\partial x}\left(k(x)\frac{\partial u}{\partial x}\right)-q(x)u$$

$$(k(x)>0,\quad q(x)\geqslant 0,\quad \rho(x)>0)$$

Show that the eigenfunctions of the problem are orthogonal with weight $\rho(x)$ in the interval $[0,\ l]$ and that the eigenvalues are all positive.

## 2. Problems associated with the two-dimensional wave equation; Laplace's equation, and Poisson's equation

**168.** (a) Find the natural frequencies of vibration of a rectangular membrane with sides $l_1$ and $l_2$ that is fastened along the edges. Consider the case in which $l_1=l_2$.

(b) Find the frequency of the fundamental tone of a square membrane of side $l$ that is fastened along the edges.

**169.** Find the eigenvalues and eigenfunctions of the boundary-value problem

$$\Delta v+\lambda v=0\quad (v=v(x,\ y);\ 0\leqslant x\leqslant a;\ 0\leqslant y\leqslant b)$$

$$v|_{x=0}=v|_{x=a}=v|_{y=0}=v|_{y=b}=0.$$

**170.** A homogeneous square membrane is fastened along its edges. If its shape at the initial instant $t=0$ is given by $u(x,\ y,\ 0)=Axy(l-x)(l-y)$, where $A$ = const., and if its initial velocity is zero, find the free vibrations of the membrane.

**171.** Solve the boundary-value problem

$$\varphi_{tt}=a^2(\varphi_{xx}+\varphi_{yy})\quad \begin{pmatrix}0<x<l_1\\0<y<l_2\end{pmatrix};\ t>0$$

$$\varphi|_{x=0}=\varphi|_{x=l_1}=\varphi|_{y=0}=\varphi|_{y=l_2}=0$$

$$\varphi(x,\ y,\ 0)=0,\quad \varphi_t(x,\ y,\ 0)=Axy(l_1-x)(l_2-y)$$

$$\begin{pmatrix}0<x<l_1\\0<y<l_2\end{pmatrix},\quad A=\text{const.}$$

**172.** Suppose that a rectangular membrane $0 \leqslant x \leqslant l_1$, $0 \leqslant y \leqslant l_2$ is fastened along the edges. Find the transverse vibrations caused by a force of density

$$F(x, y, t) = A(x, y) \sin \omega t \quad (t > 0).$$

applied perpendicularly to the surface of the membrane. Consider the resonant case.

**173.** Solve the boundary-value problem

$$\Delta u = \frac{\partial^2 u}{\partial x^2} + \frac{\partial^2 u}{\partial y^2} = 0 \quad (0 \leqslant x \leqslant a;\ 0 \leqslant y \leqslant b)$$

$$u|_{x=0} = v = \text{const.},\ u|_{x=a} = u|_{y=0} = 0,\ u|_{y=b} = v_0 = \text{const.}$$

**174.** Find the harmonic function $\varphi(x, y)$ inside the rectangle $0 \leqslant x \leqslant a$, $0 \leqslant y \leqslant b$, if its values on the boundary are given:

$$\varphi|_{x=0} = Ay(b-y), \quad \varphi|_{x=a} = 0 \quad (0 \leqslant y \leqslant b),$$
$$\varphi|_{y=0} = B \sin \frac{\pi x}{a}, \quad \varphi|_{y=b} = 0 \quad (0 \leqslant x \leqslant a),$$

where $A$ and $B$ are constants.

**175.** Find the electrostatic field inside the region bounded by conducting plates $y = 0$, $y = b$, and $x = 0$ $(x > 0)$, if the plate $x = 0$ is charged to a potential $v_0 = \text{const.}$, if the plases $y = 0$ and $y = b$ are grounded, and if there are no charges inside the region in question.

**176.** Find the potential of an electrostatic field $u(x, y)$ inside a rectangular box, $0 \leqslant x \leqslant a$, $-b/2 \leqslant y \leqslant b/2$ (see Fig. 7) if the potentials on its edges are as follows:

$$U = \begin{cases} \varphi_1(x) & \text{for } y = \frac{b}{2}, \\ \varphi_2(x) & \text{for } y = -\frac{b}{2}, \\ \psi_1(y) & \text{for } x = 0, \\ \psi_2(y) & \text{for } x = a \end{cases}$$

and if there are no charges inside the box.

**177.** Find the solution of the equation

$$\Delta u = -y \cos x$$

inside the semicircle $x^2 + y^2 < 1$, $y > 0$ that satisfies the conditions

$$u = 0 \quad \text{for} \quad y = 0,$$
$$u = \sqrt{1 - x^2}\left(\cos x - \frac{1}{2}\right) \quad \text{for} \quad y > 0.$$

on the boundary.

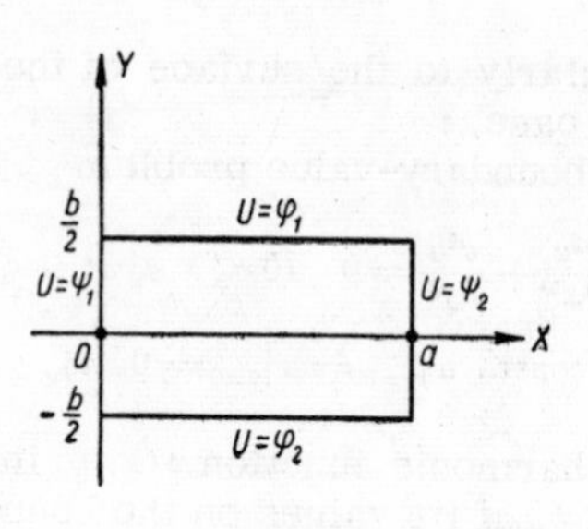


FIG. 7

**178.** We know that the problem of torsion of an arbitrary prismatic body whose cross section is a region $D$ bounded by a contour $L$ leads to the following boundary-value problem: Find the solution of Poisson's equation

$$\Delta u = -2,$$

that vanishes on the contour $L$. Here, the basic quantities needed for the analysis are the components $\tau_{zx}$ and $\tau_{zy}$, of the shear stress and the twisting moment $M$. These are expressed in terms of a stress function $u$ as follows:

$$\tau_{zx} = G\Theta \frac{\partial u}{\partial y}, \quad \tau_{zy} = -G\Theta \frac{\partial u}{\partial x},$$
$$M = 2G\Theta \iint_{(D)} u \, dx \, dy,$$

where $\Theta$ is the angle of twist per unit length and $G$ is the modulus of shear.

Give a direct solution of the problem (that is, find the stress function, $\tau_{zx}$, $\tau_{zy}$ and $M$) for the torsion of the rectangle

$$D\begin{pmatrix} 0 \leqslant x \leqslant a \\ 0 \leqslant y \leqslant b \end{pmatrix}.$$

**179*.** Find the static deflection of a rectangular membrane with sides $2a$ and $2b$ under the action of a line load uniformly distributed along the axis of symmetry as shown in Fig. 8. The edges of the membrane are rigidly fastened.

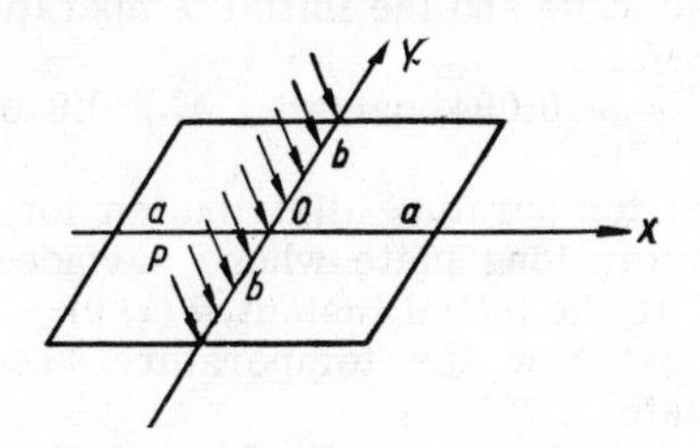


FIG. 8

**180*.** Suppose that a variable external pressure $P_0(x, y, t)$ is applied to the surface of a liquid in a rectangular container $0 \leqslant x \leqslant a$, $0 \leqslant y \leqslant b$. Suppose that, as a result of this pressure, a wave motion is generated such that the motion of the particles of the liquid is horizontal and independent of the depth. The depth of the liquid in its undisturbed state is equal to $h$. Find the potential $u(x, y, t)$ of the horizontal velocities of the particles of the liquid if the initial state is given by

$$u(x, y, 0) = u_t(x, y, 0) = 0.$$

Consider the case

$$P_0(x, y, t) = A\varphi(t) \cos\frac{\pi x}{a} \cos\frac{\pi y}{b} \qquad (A = \text{const.})$$

## 3. Problems involving equations of the heat-flow type

**181.** Solve the boundary-value problems:

(a) $\frac{\partial u}{\partial t} = a^2 \frac{\partial^2 u}{\partial x^2}$, $(0 < x < l,\ t > 0)$. $u(x, 0) = \frac{cx(l-x)}{l^2}$, $u(0, t) = u(l, t) = 0$;

(b) $\frac{\partial u}{\partial t} = a^2 \frac{\partial^2 u}{\partial x^2}$, $(0 < x < l,\ t > 0)$. $u(l, t) = u_0$, $\frac{\partial u(0, t)}{\partial x} = 0$, $u(x, 0) = \varphi(x)$.

*Hint:* Seek a solution of the form $u(x, t) = u_0 + v(x, t)$, where $v(x, t)$ is an unknown function.

(c) $\frac{\partial v}{\partial t} = a^2 \frac{\partial^2 v}{\partial x^2} + A\omega\left(\frac{x}{l} - 1\right) \cos \omega t$, $(0 < x < l, t > 0)$. $v(0, t) = 0$, $v(l, t) = 0$, $v(x, 0) = 0$.

**182.** Find the temperature at each point of an insulated copper rod of length $l = 100$ cm if the temperature at the ends of the rod is held at 0° and the initial temperature in the rod is $\mu(x) = 50° \sin 2\pi x/l$.

For copper, $c = 0.094$ cal/gm, $k = 0.9$ cal-sec/cm, and $\rho = 8.9$ gm/cm$^3$.

**183.** Find the temperature distribution for positive values of $t$ in an infinitely long plate whose surfaces $x = 0$ and $x = l$ are insulated if at the initial instant, $T(x, 0) = A \sin x(l - x)/l$; that is, show just how the temperature becomes equalized throughout the plate.

**184.** If a thread of very small cross section is bent to form a closed circle, it is called a ring. In a certain ring of length $2\pi$, an initial temperature distribution $f(x)$ is given. If the ring is allowed to cool freely, what will the temperature distribution be after an arbitrary interval of time?

**185.** (The problem of the cooling of a sphere.) A sphere of radius $R$ is immersed in a medium at temperature 0°. The initial temperature at each point of the sphere is given by $f(r)$, where $r$ denotes the distance from the center of the sphere. On the surface of the sphere, the cooling proceeds according to Newton's law:

$$\left(\frac{\partial u}{\partial r} + hu\right)\Big|_{r=R} = 0,$$

where $h$ is a positive constant.

Study the process of cooling of the sphere for $t > 0$.

**186.** Derive the equation for diffusion in a hollow tube (without sources of matter) when there is no diffusion through the walls of the tube:

$$C\frac{\partial u}{\partial t} = \frac{\partial}{\partial x}\left(D\frac{\partial u}{\partial x}\right),$$

where $D$ is the coefficient of diffusion, $C$ is the coefficient of porosity, and $u = u(x, t)$ is the concentration of the substance in the cross section $x$ at the instant $t$. If $C$ and $D$ are constants, the equation then takes the form

$$\frac{\partial u}{\partial t} = a^2\frac{\partial^2 u}{\partial x^2}.$$

(See Tikhonov and Samarskiy, *Uravneniya matematicheskoy fiziki* [Equations of Mathematical Physics].)

**187.** Suppose that a sphere of radius $R$ with initial temperature distribution $f(r)$ is given. At an initial instant of time, the sphere is dipped into icewater, so that the surface temperature is maintained at 0°C. Find the temperature distribution within the sphere at any subsequent instant. The cooling proceeds uniformly since the temperature depends only on the radius-vector $r$ and the time $t$. Consider the case in which $f(r)=t_0=$ const.

**188.** One end of a rod $x=0$ is thermally isolated and the other $x=l$ is held at 0°. At the instant $t=0$, the temperature has the same value $T_0$ at all points of the rod. Determine the temperature $u(x, t)$ at every point $x$ at an arbitrary subsequent instant of time.

**189.** Solve the boundary-value problem

$$\begin{aligned} &u_t=a^2u_{xx}+g(x, t), && (0<x<l,\ 0<t<\infty) \\ &u|_{t=0}=f(x), && (0<x<l) \\ &u_x|_{x=0}=0, && (0<t<\infty) \\ &h(u|_{x=l}-u_l)=-ku_x|_{x=l} && (u_l=u_l(t)). \end{aligned}$$

Give a physical interpretation of this problem.

**190.** Set up the one-dimensional heat-flow equation taking account of the heat exchange through the lateral surface of a homogeneous rod.

**191.** Find the steady-state temperature distribution $u(x, y)$ in an infinitely long beam of square cross section (see Fig. 9), three sides of which are held at 0° and the fourth is held at a constant temperature $u(x, a)=T$.

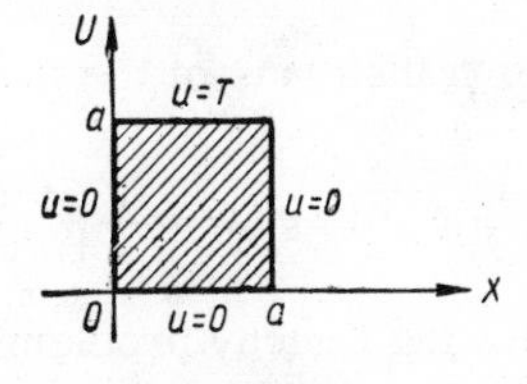


FIG. 9

**192.** Consider a rod of rectangular cross section, two opposite sides of which $y=0$ and $y=b$ are held respectively at temperatures 0° and $T=$ const. and the other two sides $(x=\pm a)$ radiate heat into the surrounding medium according to Newton's law. If the temperature of this medium is 0°, find the temperature at the point $(0, b/2)$ of the rod.

**193.** Find the temperature of a rod $0 \leqslant x \leqslant l$ with thermally insulated lateral surface if the initial temperature is everywhere zero, if the temperature at the ends is held at zero, and if a source of constant strength $Q$ is concentrated at the point $x_0$ (where $0 < x_0 < l$) in the rod.

## 4. Fourier integrals and the Fourier transformation

**194.** Represent the function

$$f(x)=\begin{cases}1 & \text{for } |x|<1,\\ \frac{1}{2} & \text{for } |x|=1,\\ 0 & \text{for } |x|>1.\end{cases}$$

by means of a Fourier integral. Show that

$$\int_0^\infty \frac{\sin t}{t}\,dt=\frac{\pi}{2}.$$

**195.** Determine the functions $f(x)$ and $\varphi(x)$ from the following relations:

$$\int_0^\infty f(x)\cos\lambda x\,dx=\frac{k}{k^2+\lambda^2},\quad \int_0^\infty \varphi(x)\sin\lambda x\,dx=\frac{\lambda}{k^2+\lambda^2}.$$

**196.** Show that the functions

$$\bar{f}(\lambda)=e^{-a\lambda^2},\quad \bar{g}(\lambda)=\frac{1}{\lambda^2+h^2}$$

are the Fourier cosine transforms of the functions

$$f(x)=\frac{1}{\sqrt{2a}}e^{-\frac{x^2}{4a}},\quad g(x)=\frac{1}{h}\sqrt{\frac{\pi}{2}}\,e^{-hx}.$$

**197.** Solve the following Cauchy problems

(a) $u_{tt}=a^2u_{xx}+xt, \qquad (-\infty<x<\infty,\ t>0)$

$u(x,0)=0,\ u_t(x,0)=0, \quad (-\infty<x<\infty).$

(b) $u_t=a^2u_{xx}, \qquad (-\infty<x<\infty,\ t>0)$

$u(x,0)=\mu(x), \qquad (-\infty<x<\infty).$

Evaluate the unknown function when $\mu(x)=T_0=\text{const}$.

(c) $u_t=a^2u_{xx}+f(x,t), \quad (-\infty<x<\infty,\ t>0)$

$u(x,0)=\mu(x).$

**198.** Solve the following boundary-value problems:

(a) $u_{tt} = a^2 u_{xx}$, $(0 < x,\ t < \infty)$
$u(0,\ t) = t^2$, $(0 < t < \infty)$
$u(x,\ 0) = u_t(x,\ 0) = 0$, $(0 < x < \infty)$.

(b) $u_t = a^2 u_{xx}$, $(0 < x,\ t < \infty)$
$u(0,\ t) = 0$, $(0 < t < \infty)$
$u(x,\ 0) = f(x)$, $(0 < x < \infty)$.

(c) $u_t = a^2 u_{xx}$, $(0 < x,\ t < \infty)$
$u_x(0,\ t) = 0$, $u(x,\ 0) = f(x)$.

**199.** Find the solution of Laplace's equation

$$\frac{\partial^2 u}{\partial x^2} + \frac{\partial^2 u}{\partial y^2} = 0 \quad (0 \leqslant x < \infty,\ 0 \leqslant y < \infty)$$

with boundary conditions

$$u|_{y=0} = 0, \quad \left.\frac{\partial u}{\partial x}\right|_{x=0} = f(y).$$

**200.** Find the solution of the heat-flow equation in a homogeneous rod in a medium of temperature $U$:

$$\frac{\partial u}{\partial t} - a^2 \frac{\partial^2 u}{\partial x^2} - b^2 (U - u) = g(x,\ t) \ (-\infty < x < \infty,\ t > 0)$$

with the initial condition $u(x,\ 0) = f(x)$. Consider this problem when $U = U_\infty =$ const. and there are no heat sources.

# CHAPTER 6

## *Problems Involving Special Functions*

**201.** Euler's gamma function is defined for all positive $p$ by the convergent improper integral

$$\Gamma(p) = \int_0^\infty x^{p-1} e^{-x}\, dx.$$

Show that $\Gamma(p+1) = p\Gamma(p)$ for arbitrary real $p$. Derive the formula

$$\Gamma(n+1) = n! = \int_0^\infty x^n e^{-x}\, dx \qquad (n = 1,\ 2,\ 3,\ \ldots).$$

**202.** Prove the identities

(a) $J_{-n}(x) = (-1)^n J_n(x) \quad (n = 1,\ 2,\ 3,\ \ldots).$

(b) $J_1(x) = -J_0'(x);\ [xJ_1(x)]' = xJ_0(x).$

(c) $\int_0^x \xi J_0(\xi)\, d\xi = xJ_1(x)$

$\int_0^x \xi J_0^2(a\xi)\, d\xi = \frac{x^2}{2}[J_0^2(ax) + J_1^2(ax)]$

$\int_0^x \xi^3 J_0(\xi)\, d\xi = 2x^2 J_0(x) + (x^3 - 4x) J_1(x).$

(d) $\frac{d}{dx}[x^p J_p(x)] = x^p J_{p-1}(x);$

$\frac{d}{dx}[x^{-p} J_p(x)] = -x^{-p} J_{p+1}(x)$

for arbitrary $p$.

(e) $xJ_p'(x)+pJ_p(x)=xJ_{p-1}(x)$,

$xJ_p'(x)-pJ_p(x)=-xJ_{p+1}(x)$,

$J_{p-1}(x)-J_{p+1}(x)=2J_p'(x)$,

$J_{p-1}(x)+J_{p+1}(x)=\frac{2p}{x}J_p(x)$

for arbitrary $p$. By setting $p=n-1$ (for $n=1, 2, 3, \ldots$) in the last relationship, derive the recursion formula

$$J_n(x)=\frac{2n-2}{x}J_{n-1}(x)-J_{n-2}(x) \quad (n=2, 3, 4, \ldots).$$

Express $J_2(x)$, $J_3(x)$, and $J_4(x)$ in terms of $J_0(x)$ and $J_1(x)$.

**203.** Find expressions for $J_{\frac{1}{2}}(x)$, $J_{-\frac{1}{2}}(x)$, $J_{\frac{3}{2}}(x)$.

**204.** Integrate the equations:

(a) $\frac{1}{x}\frac{d}{dx}\left(x\frac{dy}{dx}\right)+\left(\alpha^2-\frac{n^2}{x^2}\right)y=0 \quad (n=0, 1, 2, \ldots)$.

(b) $y''+\frac{1}{x}y'-\left(1+\frac{n^2}{x^2}\right)y=0 \quad (n=0, 1, 2, \ldots)$,

$y''+xy=0$.

(c) $y''+\frac{5}{x}y'+y=0$.

**205.** Prove the relations

$$\int_0^l J_n\left(\frac{\alpha_{mn}}{l}x\right)J_n\left(\frac{\alpha_{pn}}{l}\right)dx=\begin{cases}0, & \text{if} \quad m\neq p,\\ \frac{l^2}{2}J_n'^2(\alpha_{mn}), & \text{if} \quad m=p,\end{cases}$$

where the $\alpha_{mn}$ are the positive roots of the equation $J_n(\alpha)=0$, the subscript $m$ indicating the ordinal number of the root.

**206.** Expand the following functions in Fourier-Bessel series:

(a) $f(x)=x^p$ (for $p\geqslant-1/2$) in a series of the functions $J_p(\lambda_1 x)$, $J_p(\lambda_2 x)$, ... in the interval $0<x<1$ (where the $\lambda_i$ are the positive roots of the equation $J_p(\lambda)=0$).

(b) $f(x)=x^3$ in a series of the functions $\{J_3(\lambda_i x)\}$ in the interval $0<x<2$ (where $J_3(\lambda_i)=0$ for $\lambda_i>0$ with $i=1, 2, 3, \ldots$).

**207.** Use Rodrigues' formula for the Legendre polynomials

$$P_n(x)=\frac{1}{2^n n!}\frac{d^n(x^2-1)^n}{dx^n},$$

to find the first five Legendre polynomials and draw their graphs.

**208.** The Legendre polynomials may be defined as the coefficients of $r^n$ in the expansion of the generating function $(1 - 2rx + r^2)^{-\frac{1}{2}}$ in a series of powers of $r$ (where $|x| \leqslant 1$ and $|r| < 11$):

$$(1 - 2rx + r^2)^{-\frac{1}{2}} = \sum_{n=0}^{\infty} P_n(x) r^n, \tag{1}$$

$$P_n(x) = \sum_{k=0} (-1)^k \frac{1 \cdot 3 \cdot 5 \ldots (2n - 2k - 1)}{2^k \cdot k! \, (n - 2k)!} x^{n-2k}.$$

Evaluate $P_n(1)$, $P_n(-1)$, and $P_n(0)$.
Derive the recursion formula

$$(n+1) P_{n+1} + (2n+1) x P_n - n P_{n-1} = 0 \; (n = 1, 2, 3 \ldots).$$

by differentiating the relation (1) with respect to $r$ and equating terms of like powers of $r^n$ on the two sides of the equation.

**209.** Expand the functions

$$\varphi(r, \theta) = \left(1 - 2\left(\frac{1}{r}\right) \cos\theta + \left(\frac{1}{r}\right)^2\right)^{-\frac{1}{2}}$$

and

$$f(x) = \begin{cases} 0 & \text{for} \quad -1 \leqslant x < 0, \\ 1 & \text{for} \quad 0 < x \leqslant 1 \end{cases}$$

in a series of Legendre polynomials.

**210.** Prove the identities:

(a) $P_{2n+1}(0) = 0, \; P_{2n}(0) = (-1)^n \dfrac{1 \cdot 3 \cdot 5 \ldots (2n-1)}{2 \cdot 4 \ldots 2n}$.

(b) $P_{n-1}(0) - P_{n+1}(0) = \dfrac{2n+1}{n+1} P_{n-1}(0)$.

(c) $(2n+1) P_n(x) = P'_{n+1}(x) - P'_{n-1}(x)$.

(d) $\displaystyle\int_{-1}^{1} P_n(x) P_m(x)\, dx = \begin{cases} 0, & \text{if} \quad n \neq m \\ \dfrac{2}{2n+1}, & \text{if} \quad n = m. \end{cases}$

(e) $\displaystyle\int_0^1 P_n(x)\, dx = \begin{cases} 1 & \text{for} \quad n = 0 \\ 0 & \text{for} \quad n \geqslant 2 \text{ and even}, \\ (-1)^{\frac{n-1}{2}} \cdot \dfrac{3 \cdot 5 \cdot 7 \ldots (n-2)}{2 \cdot 4 \cdot 6 \ldots (n+1)} & \\ \quad \text{for} \quad n \geqslant 1 \text{ and odd.} & \end{cases}$

**211.** Find the bounded solutions of Laplace's equation

$$\frac{\partial}{\partial r}\left(r^2\frac{\partial u}{\partial r}\right)+\frac{1}{\sin\theta}\frac{\partial}{\partial\theta}\left(\sin\theta\frac{\partial u}{\partial\theta}\right)=0$$

inside and outside a sphere of radius $R$ if the solutions are equal to a function $f(\theta)$ on its surface. Carry out the calculations for $r<R=1$ and $f(\theta)=\cos^2\theta$.

**212.** Examine the axially symmetric vibrations of a circular membrane of radius $R$ that are caused by an impulse $P$ applied at the instant $t=0$ and distributed over a circular area of radius $\varepsilon$. The membrane is fastened along its edge.

**213.** Determine the form of forced vibrations of a circular membrane of radius $R$ that is fastened along its edge if a pulsating load is uniformly distributed over its surface according to the law $q\sin(\omega t+\psi)$ (where $q$ is a constant).

**214.** Suppose that a weight is applied at the instant $t=0$ to a circular membrane of radius $R$. If the weight is uniformly distributed with density $q(t)$ over the annulus $r_1<r<r_2$, determine the form of the membrane for $t>0$. Assume that the membrane is fastened along the edge.

**215.** A homogeneous circular membrane of radius $R$ has the form of a paraboloid of revolution

$$u(r,\ 0)=u_0(r)=b\left(1-\frac{r^2}{R^2}\right),$$

at an initial instant $t=0$, where $b$ is the initial deviation of the center $r=0$. The initial velocities and the boundary condition are given in the form

$$\left.\frac{\partial u}{\partial t}\right|_{t=0}=v_0(r)=0;\quad u(R,\ t)=0.$$

Find the displacement of the center $r=0$ of the membrane at an arbitrary instant $t>0$. Calculate the period of the fundamental tone of the membrane, assuming that it is made of paper of thickness 0.2 mm. The radius $R=5$ cm, and the tension is $T=100$ gm/cm. The density of paper is 1 gm/cm$^2$.

**216.** A sphere of radius $R$ is placed in an irrotational parallel flow of an incompressible liquid moving with a constant velocity $a$. Study the distribution of the velocities in this flow.

**217.** Study the free radial vibrations of a circular membrane of radius $R$ fastened along its edge with arbitrary initial conditions. Also, carry out the calculations for the case in which the initial displacement is $f(r)=r^2$ and the initial velocity is $g(r)=r^2$.

**218.** Determine the natural frequencies of the radial vibrations of the circular membrane of problem 217 and also the amplitude of the vibrations of each tone.

**219.** Consider an infinitely long cylinder of radius $a$ the lateral surface of which is thermally insulated. Find the temperature as a function of position and time if the initial temperature is axially symmetric and is given by $u(r, 0)=r^2$.

**220.** Solve the boundary-value problem

$$\frac{\partial^2 w}{\partial t^2}=a^2\left\{\frac{1}{r^2}\frac{\partial}{\partial r}\left(r^2\frac{\partial w}{\partial r}\right)-\frac{2w}{r^2}\right\}\quad\begin{pmatrix}0\leqslant r\leqslant r_0,\\ t>0\end{pmatrix},$$

$$w'_r(r_0, t)=0\quad(t>0),$$

$$w(r, 0)=vr,\quad w'_t(r, 0)=0\quad(0\leqslant r\leqslant r_0,\ v=\text{const.}).$$

by the method of separation of variables.

**221.** Suppose that a spherical vessel containing a liquid (gas) is in uniform motion with velocity $v$. If at the instant $t=0$ the vessel suddenly stops, find the resulting vibrations in the fluid.

**222.** Suppose that the temperature in an infinitely long cylinder of radius $R$ is radially distributed and given by a function $f(r)$. At an initial instant, the surface of the cylinder is suddenly cooled to 0° and is then held at that value. Find the temperature distribution inside the cylinder at an arbitrary instant of time. Consider the case in which $f(r)=t_0=$ const.

**223.** Show that the function

$$u_n=\left(c_{1n}r^n+\frac{c_{2n}}{r^{n+1}}\right)Y_n(\Theta, \varphi)$$

is a particular solution of Laplace's equation $\Delta u(r, \Theta, \varphi)=0$ (where the $c_{in}$, for $i=1, 2$, are arbitrary constants).

**224.** A homogeneous circular membrane of radius $R$ is fastened along its edge. It is in equilibrium under tension $T$. At an instant $t=0$, a uniformly distributed pulsating load $P_0 \sin \omega t$ is applied to the surface of the membrane. Find the radial vibrations of the membrane.

**225.** Find the potential of the horizontal velocities of water particles vibrating in a right circular cylinder with horizontal base if the initial conditions possess radial symmetry and the pressure on the surface of the water is constant.

**226.** A spherical conductor is partitioned into two hemispheres by a layer of insulating material. The upper hemisphere is charged to a potential $U_1$ and the lower to a potential $U_2$. Find the potential of such a conductor at an arbitrary point $M$ of the electrostatic field (see Fig. 10).

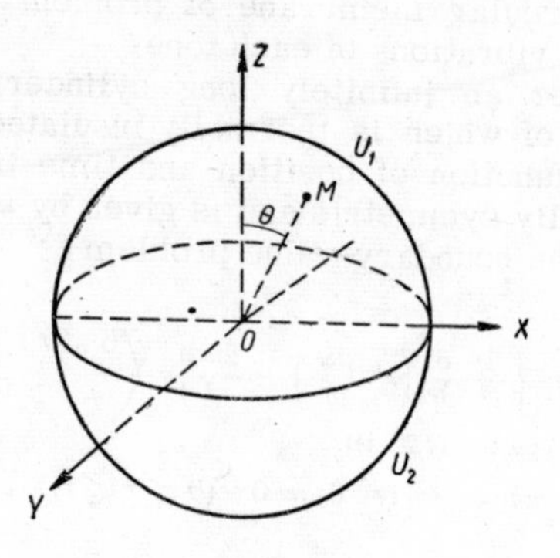


FIG. 10

**227.** A homogeneous $n$th degree polynomial $U_n$ satisfying Laplace's equation $\Delta u(x, y, z) = 0$ is called a *harmonic polynomial.* Obviously, the polynomials

$$U_0 = a,$$
$$U_1 = ax + by + cz$$

are polynomials of degree 0 and 1.

Find the general form of the second- and third-degree harmonic polynomials $U_2$ and $U_3$. Show that the spherical functions

$$r^m Y_{mh}(\Theta, \varphi) = r^m P_{mh}(\cos\Theta) \begin{Bmatrix} \sinh\varphi \\ \cosh\varphi \end{Bmatrix}$$

are harmonic polynomials of degree $m$.

# PART III

## The Elements of Probability Theory

CHAPTER 7

## 1. The basic concepts and theorems of probability theory. The binomial distribution

**228.** Someone fires at a target three times. Consider the following simple events: $A_i$ (for $i = 1, 2, 3$) denotes a hit on the $i$th shot: $\bar{A}_i$ denotes a miss on the $i$th shot. What do the following events denote?

(1) $B = A_1\bar{A}_2\bar{A}_3 + \bar{A}_1A_2\bar{A}_3 + \bar{A}_1\bar{A}_2A_3$

(2) $C = A_1A_2\bar{A}_3 + A_1\bar{A}_2A_3 + \bar{A}_1A_2A_3 + A_1A_2A_3$

**229.** What do the following events represent?

(1) $(A+B)(B+C)$; (2) $A(B+C)+(A+B)C$; (3) $(A+\bar{B})(\bar{A}+B)$; (4) $\overline{AB}$; (5) $\overline{A+B}$; (6) $\overline{\bar{A}\bar{B}}$; (7) $\overline{\bar{A}+\bar{B}}$?

**230.** What do the following events represent?

(1) $(A+B)(A+\bar{B})+\bar{A}$;

(2) $(A+B)(A+\bar{B})(\bar{A}+B)(\bar{A}+\bar{B})$

**231.** Each of the six letters, $A$, $K$, $S$, $O$, $M$, $B$ is written on a card. The cards are then selected at random, one at a time, and laid out in the order of selection. What is the probability of obtaining the word MOSKVA?

**232.** An electric power line joining two points $A$ and $B$ breaks down somewhere in the middle. What is the probability that the breakdown is farther than 450 meters from point $A$ if the distance between A and B is 2 kilometers?

**233.** An urn contains 20 white, 45 black, and 35 red balls. What is the probability that a ball taken at random from the urn will be red?

**234.** Suppose that 10 items in a lot of 300 are damaged. If an item is taken at random from the lot, what is the probability that it will be one of the damaged ones?

**235.** A box contains $N$ items, of which $M$ are good and $L$ defective. Someone takes $n$ (where $n < N$) items at random from the box without returning them. Find the probability $P_m$ that $m$ of the items taken out will be good.

Using the results obtained, derive the following identity involving such combinations:

$$\sum_{m=0}^{M} C_M^m \cdot C_{N-M}^{n-m} = C_N^n$$

**236.** A region $D$ of area $S$ contains a circle $C$ of radius $R$ with center at the point $A$. Suppose that $N$ points are chosen at random in $D$. What is the probability that at least one of these points will be inside the circle $C$?

**237.** If $A$ and $B$ are two events, show that

$$P(A+B)=P(A)+P(B)-P(AB)$$

Generalize this equation to an arbitrary finite number of events:

$$P\left(\sum_{i=1}^{n} A_i\right)=\sum_{i=1}^{n} P(A_i)-\sum_{i,j=1}^{n} P(A_iA_j)+$$

$$+\sum_{i,j,k=1}^{n} P(A_iA_jA_k)+\ldots+(-1)^{n-1}\cdot P(A_1A_2\ldots A_n)$$

**238.** An urn contains 5 white and 3 black balls. Two balls are taken from the urn, one after the other. Find the probability that both balls will be white. Solve the problem both under the hypothesis that the first ball is not returned to the urn and then under the hypothesis that it *is* returned.

**239.** In a lot of 200 objects, 150 are of first grade, 30 are of second grade, 16 are of third grade, and 4 are rejects. What is the probability that an object chosen at random will be either of first or of second grade?

**240.** An urn contains white, black, red, and green balls. The probability of taking a white ball at random is 0.15, a black ball 0.23, and a red ball 0.17. What is the probability of taking a green ball?

**241.** Someone fires at a circular target consisting of three zones: I, II, III (see Fig. 11). The probability of his scoring a hit in the first zone is 0.25, in the second zone 0.35, and in the third zone 0.15. What is the probability of his missing the target entirely?

**242.** Two dice are thrown. What are the probabilities that (a) the sum of the spots thrown will be a multiple of 3, (b) the sum will be equal to 7 and the difference will be equal to 3, (c) the sum will be equal to 7 when it is known that the difference is 3?

**243.** An airplane is fired on three times. The probabilities of a hit are, in the three cases, 0.4, 0.5, and 0.7. What is the probability that *exactly* one hit will be scored? What is the probability that *at least* one hit will be scored?

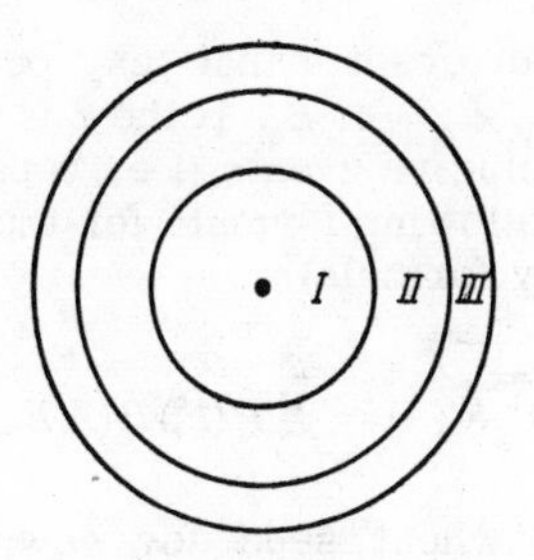


FIG. 11

**244.** Consider two lots of objects:

1st lot

| Grade | Number of objects |
|---|---|
| I | 8 |
| II | 3 |
| III | 1 |
| Rejects | 1 |
| Total | 13 |

2nd lot

| Grade | Number of objects |
|---|---|
| I | 12 |
| II | 2 |
| III | 1 |
| Rejects | 2 |
| Total | 17 |

One object is chosen at random from each lot. What is the probability that these two objects chosen will both be grade I?

**245.** Suppose that the conditions of the preceding problem are modified as follows: both objects are chosen from the first lot and the first object chosen is returned before the second object is chosen. What is the probability that the first object will be grade I and that the second will be grade II?

**246.** As a second modification, suppose that three objects are chosen, all from the first lot, and that each object is returned before another selection is made. Find the probability that all three objects will be grade I.

**247.** A student seeking a particular book decides to try three libraries. In each case, there is a fifty-fifty chance that the library has the book, and, if so, the chances are fifty-fifty that someone already has the book out. What is more probable: that the student will find the book, or that he will not?

**248.** One marksman hits a target 80% of the time; another hits it 70% of the time. If both fire at the target, what is the probability that at least one will hit it?

**249.** Consider an event $A$ that may occur together with one of a set of events $E_1, E_2, \ldots, E_n$. If the $E$'s constitute a complete set of mutually exclusive events (i.e., a partition of the sample space), prove the following formula for the probability of $A$ (the complete probability formula):

$$P(A) = \sum_{i=1}^{n} P(E_i) P(A/E_i)$$

**250.** A bag of wheat seed for sowing that is classified grade I contains small admixtures of grade II, III, and IV seeds. The probability that an individual seed taken at random will be grade I is 0.96; that it will be grade II is 0.01; that it will be grade III, 0.02; that it will be grade IV, 0.01. Suppose that the conditional probability that a seed that *is* grade I will yield a stalk containing no fewer than 50 seeds is 0.50; for a grade II seed, the figure is 0.15; for a grade III seed, it is 0.20; for a grade IV seed, it is 0.05. Find the unconditional probability that a seed chosen at random will yield a stalk with at least 50 seeds.

**251.** Suppose that each of six identical boxes contains 15 objects and that the number of first-grade objects in each is given by the following table:

| Box number | Number of objects | |
|---|---|---|
| | total | first-grade |
| 1 | 15 | 8 |
| 2 | 15 | 8 |
| 3 | 15 | 8 |
| 4 | 15 | 6 |
| 5 | 15 | 6 |
| 6 | 15 | 5 |

Someone takes an object at random from one of the boxes. What is the probability that he will take a first-grade object?

**252.** By using the theorem on multiplication of probabilities and the formula for total probability (see problem 249) prove the following theorem: suppose that $E_1, E_2, \ldots, E_n$ constitute a complete set of mutually exclusive events. Denote the probabilities of these events before an experiment by $P(E_1), P(E_2), \ldots, P(E_n)$. Let an experiment be performed as a result of which an event $A$ is observed to happen. Then, the probability of the event $E_i$, for $i = 1, 2, \ldots, n$, after this experiment is given by Bayes' formula

$$P(E_i/A)=\frac{P(E_i)\,P(A/E_i)}{\sum_{k=1}^{n} P(E_k)\,P(A/E_k)}$$

**253.** Two marksmen each fire a shot at a target. Suppose that the probability that the first will get a hit is 0.6 and the probability that the second will get a hit is 0.3. Suppose that after both have taken their shots, someone examines the target and finds one bullet-hole in it. What is the probability that it was made by the first marksman? By the second?

**254.** Buffon's problem. A set of parallel lines are drawn in a plane at a distance $2a$ from each other. A needle of length $2a$ (and negligible diameter) is tossed onto the plane. Show that the probability that the needle will cross one of the straight lines is equal to $2/\pi \approx 0.637$.

**255.** A box contains white, black, and red balls. The probability of taking a white, black, or red ball is respectively $p_1 = 0.15, p_2 = 0.22, p_3 = 0.12$. Find

(1) the probability of taking a white ball in a single random selection;

(2) the probability of taking a white ball in 10 random selections;

(3) the probability of taking at least one white ball in 10 random selections;

(4) the probability of taking at least 9 white balls in 10 random selections.

**256.** Suppose that

$$\varphi_n(z)=\prod_{i=1}^{n}(p_i z+q_i)$$

where $p_i$ denotes the probability of occurrence of an event $A$ in the $i$th Bernoulli trial and $q_i = 1 - p_i$.

Show that the probability that the event $A$ will occur exactly $m$ times in $n$ independent trials is equal to the coefficient of $z^m$ in the expression for the function $\varphi_n(z)$. The function $\varphi_n(z)$ is called the *generating function* of the probabilities $P_n(m)$.

Use the expansion of the generating function to solve the following problem: four persons shoot at a target from different distances. The probabilities of their scoring a hit are respectively $p_1 = 0.1$, $p_2 = 0.2$, $p_3 = 0.3$, and $p_4 = 0.4$. Find the probability of one, two, three, four, no hits.

**257.** From the data of problem 239, find the probability that in a random selection of five objects,

(1) all five objects will be of first-grade,

(2) four will be of first-grade and one will not be of first-grade,

(3) three objects will be of first-grade and two will not be of first-grade,

(4) not one of the objects will be of first-grade.

## 2. Random variables. Distribution functions. Numerical characteristics of random variables

**258.** Give some examples of discrete and continuous random variables.

What is a distribution series (or distribution table) of a random variable? Give some examples. What is the distribution function of a random variable? What are its properties? What is the probability density function of a random variable? What are its properties?

**259.** Someone fires a single shot at a target. The probability of a hit is 0.2. Write the distribution series and the distribution function of the number of hits $\xi$.

**260.** A random variable $\xi$ has the following probability density

$$f(x)=\begin{cases} a\cos x & \text{for} \quad -\frac{\pi}{2}<x<\frac{\pi}{2}; \\ 0 & \text{for} \quad x<-\frac{\pi}{2} \text{ or } x>\frac{\pi}{2} \end{cases}$$

(a) Find the coefficient $a$.

(b) Construct a graph of the probability density $f(x)$.

(c) Find the distribution function $F(x)$ and construct its graph.

(d) Find the probability that the random variable $\xi$ will fall in the interval $(0, \pi/4)$.

**261.** What is the probability that a random variable $\xi$ with probability density

$$f(x)=\frac{1}{\pi(1+x^2)}$$

will fall in the interval $(-1, +1)$?

**262.** A random variable $\xi$ is defined by the following distribution table:

| $\xi$ | 1 | 2 | 3 |
|---|---|---|---|
| p | 0 | 0.2 | 0.8 |

A second random variable $\eta$, independent of the first, is defined by the following distribution table:

| $\eta$ | 1 | 2 | 3 |
|---|---|---|---|
| $p$ | 0.2 | 0.5 | 0.3 |

Find the law of distribution for the sum $\xi+\eta$.

**263.** A coin is tossed until it falls heads. Find the average value of the number of tosses that will be necessary.

**264.** Suppose that an electric current flows through a conductor whose resistance depends on random causes and that the current strength is also randomly determined. Suppose that it is known that the average value of the resistance of the conductor is 25 ohms and that the average value of the current is 6 amps. What is the average value of the emf $\mathcal{E}$ across the conductor?

**265.** Suppose that a random variable can assume only two values: 1—if a particular event occurs and 0—if this event does not occur. Show that the mathematical expectation of this random variable is equal to the probability of the event referred to.

**266.** A box contains 500 objects, three of them grade I. Suppose that someone takes an object from the box. Find the mathematical expectation of the number of grade I objects. Compare the result with the assertion in the preceding problem.

**267.** Show that the mathematical expectation of a random variable always lies between its smallest and largest values:

$$\xi_{\min} < M\xi < \xi_{\max}$$

**268.** Show that the variance of a discrete random variable $\xi$ that assumes the values $\xi_1, \xi_2, \ldots, \xi_n$ with probabilities $p_1, p_2, \ldots, p_n$ is equal to

$$D\xi = \alpha_2 - (M\xi)^2$$

where

$$\alpha_2 = \sum_{i=1}^{n} \xi_i^2 p_i$$

**269.** Calculate the mathematical expectation and the variance of a random variable whose probability density function is

$$f(x) = \begin{cases} \dfrac{1}{\beta-\alpha} & \text{for } \alpha < x < \beta; \\ 0 & \text{for } x < \alpha \quad \text{or} \quad x > \beta \end{cases}$$

**270.** An airplane is fired upon until a hit is scored. The probability of a hit is $p$ for each shot. Find the mathematical expectation, the variance, and the standard deviation of the number of shots that are made.

**271.** An approximative measurement of the diameter $d$ of a circle indicates that $a \leqslant d \leqslant b$. For successive calculations, $d$ is treated as a random variable with a uniform law of distribution in the interval $(a, b)$. Find the mean value and the variance of the area of the circle.

**272.** Find the probability that a random variable $\xi$ with a normal Gaussian law of distribution will fall in the following intervals:

(1) $(a-\sigma,\ a+\sigma)$; (2) $(a-2\sigma,\ a+2\sigma)$; (3) $(a-3\sigma,\ a+3\sigma)$.

**273.** The law of distribution of the absolute value of the velocity $v$ of a molecule is given by the formula*

$$P(v) = 4\sqrt{\frac{a^3}{\pi}}\, v^2 e^{-av^2}$$

(The constant $a$ is determined by the temperature of the gas and the mass of the particle in question: $a = m/2kT$, where $k$ is Boltzmann's constant.)

(a) Find the mean value of the path traversed by the molecule in a unit of time (the mean free path of the molecule).

(b) Find the mean value of the kinetic energy of the molecule (the "average energy" of the molecule).

**274.** A random variable $\xi$ obeys a normal Gaussian law with known mean value $a$ and standard deviation $\sigma$. Find the probability that $\xi$ will fall in the interval $(\alpha, \beta)$. Evaluate this probability for $(\alpha, \beta) = (5, 10)$, $a = 20$, and $\sigma = 5$.

**275.** Calculate the probability that a random variable $\xi$ that obeys a normal Gaussian law will fall on a segment of length $2l$ symmetric about the center of dispersion $a$.

**276.** Suppose that a particle (for example, a molecule of gas) is, at the instant $t = 0$, at a distance $x_0$ from an infinite plane wall that exerts a repelling force on the particle when the latter is close to it. According to the theory of Brownian motion, the expression

$$w(x)\,dx = \frac{1}{2\sqrt{\pi Dt}}\left[e^{-\frac{(x-x_0)^2}{4Dt}} + e^{-\frac{(x+x_0)^2}{4Dt}}\right]dx$$

gives the probability that this particle will at any instant $t$ be at a distance between $x$ and $x+dx$ from the wall. Find the mean

---

*See, for example, G. P. Boyev, *Teoriya veroyatnostey* (Probability Theory), Gostekhizdat, 1950, p. 108.

value of the displacement, the mean value of the square of the displacement of the particle in the time $t$, and the variance of the quantity $x$.

**277.** Suppose that $\xi$ and $\eta$ are independent random variables with a uniform law of distribution, $\xi$ in the interval $(a, b)$, $\eta$ in the interval $(c, d)$ (see problem 269). Find the mean value and the variance of the product of these random variables.

**278.** A random variable $x$ is distributed according to a normal law with mean $\bar{x}$ and standard deviation $Q_x$. Show that the probability that the absolute value of the deviation $x - \bar{x}$ will be between the numbers $a$ and $b$ (where $0 < a < b$) is equal to

$$P(a < |x - \bar{x}| < b) = \Phi\left(\frac{b}{Q_x}\right) - \Phi\left(\frac{a}{Q_x}\right),$$

where

$$\Phi(t) = \frac{2}{\sqrt{2\pi}} \int_0^t e^{-\frac{z^2}{2}} dz$$

**279.** A certain object is manufactured at a factory. Its length $x$ is a random variable distributed according to a normal Gaussian law. Its mean value is 20 cm and its variance is 0.2 cm. Find the probability that the length of a particular object will be between 19.7 cm and 20.3 cm, that is, that its length will not deviate from the mean length either way by more than 0.3 cm.

**280.** With the hypotheses of the preceding problem, what precision in the length can be guaranteed with probability 0.95?

**281.** When a gun is fired, three mutually independent factors may cause the shell to veer away from the target: (1) inaccuracy in determining the position of the target, (2) error in sighting, and (3) errors resulting from causes that vary from shot to shot (the weight of the shell, atmospheric conditions, etc.). Suppose that all three of these types of error are distributed according to a normal law with mean value zero and that their probable deviations are 24 m, 8 m, and 12 m. Find the probability that the final deviation from the target will not exceed 40 m.

**282.** A random variable $\xi$ is distributed according to the law

$$f(x) = \begin{cases} 0, & \text{if} \quad x < 0 \\ \frac{1}{a} e^{-\frac{x}{a}}, & \text{if} \quad x > 0. \end{cases}$$

Find its mathematical expectation, variance, and distribution function $F(x)$ and construct its graph.

**283.** A gun is fired from a point O along the $x$-axis. The mean distance covered by a shell is $\bar{x} = 1500$ m. Assume that the distance covered $H$ is distributed according to a normal law with mean square deviation 40 m. What percent of the shells will overshoot the target by an amount between 60 and 80 meters?

**284.** In technology, we often encounter a distribution of (necessarily positive) quantities $\xi$ according to Maxwell's law:

$$f(t) = \frac{2}{\sqrt{2\pi}} \cdot \frac{t^2}{\alpha} e^{-\frac{t^2}{2}},$$

where $\alpha$ is the parameter of the distribution, equal to $0.6267\ M\xi$.

Show that

(1) the variance of a random variable that obeys Maxwell's law is equal to $(3 - 8/\pi)\ \alpha^2 = 0.454\alpha^2$;

(2) the distribution function is given by

$$F(t) = \Phi(t) - 2t\varphi(t),$$

where

$$\Phi(t) = \frac{2}{\sqrt{2\pi}} \int_0^t e^{-\frac{t^2}{2}} dt, \quad \varphi(t) = \frac{1}{\sqrt{2\pi}} e^{-\frac{t^2}{2}}.$$

## 3. Limit theorems in probability theory

**285.** The probability of a certain event is equal to 0.005. What is the probability that this event will occur exactly 40 times when 10,000 trials are performed?

**286.** Suppose that 40% of a certain lot of articles are of first grade. If 50 objects are chosen in succession with each object returned before the next is chosen, what is the probability that exactly 25 of those chosen will be of first grade?

**287.** In problem 285, find the probability that the event will occur no more than 70 times.

**288.** Suppose that 100 series of bombs are dropped on a strip of enemy fortifications. With each such series, the mathematical expectation of the number of hits is 2 and the mean square deviation of the number of hits is 1.5. Find approximately the probability that with 100 such series the number of bombs that will hit the strip will be between 180 and 200.

**289.** An urn contains white and black balls. The probability of taking a white ball at random is $p = 0.75$.

(a) What is the probability that 8 out of 10 randomly chosen balls will be white?

Evaluate the probability that, out of 100 randomly chosen balls (with replacement), the number of white balls will be

(b) no fewer than 70 and no more than 80;

(c) no fewer than 81;

(d) no more than 70.

(e) What is the probability that, out of 400 balls chosen at random (with replacement) the relative frequency of appearance of a white ball will deviate from $p$ by an amount less than 0.035?

**290.** Suppose that a lot of 500 objects contains 300 that are of first grade. If 150 objects are chosen at random with replacement, what is the probability that the number of first-grade objects chosen will be

(a) between 78 and 102?

(b) between 78 and 108?

**291.** Use Laplace's local theorem to find the probability that, out of 10,000 births, 4,800 will be girls if the probability of the birth of a girl is $p = 0.485$.

**292.** Suppose that the probability of occurrence of a certain event is $p = 0.3$ in each of 2500 independent trials. Use Laplace's integral theorem to find the probability that the event will occur no fewer than 1500 and no more than 2000 times.

**293.** The average percent of rejects among certain manufactured articles is 3%. How large must a sample of these objects be for the probability that the deviation of the frequency of occurrence of rejects from the value 0.03 will not exceed 0.02 to be 0.9? (Use Laplace's integral theorem.)

**294.** (a) The probability of occurrence of an event $A$ in each of $n$ independent trials is $p$. If the number of trials is increased indefinitely, the frequency $m/n$ of the event $A$ converges in probability to its probability $p$; that is, for arbitrary $\varepsilon > 0$,

$$\lim_{n\to\infty} P\left\{\left|\frac{m}{n} - p\right| < \varepsilon\right\} = 1$$

(Jakok Bernoulli's theorem). Prove this by using Laplace's integral theorem.

(b) The probability of occurrence of an event in a single trial is $p = 0.6$. Use Bernoulli's theorem to find the smallest number $n$ of independent trials that will make the probability of the inequality $|m/n - 0.6| < 0.1$ exceed 0.97.

(c) If $p = 0.8$, what is the lowest number $n$ of independent trials that will verify the inequality $P\left\{\left|\frac{m}{n} - p\right| \leqslant 0.05\right\} > 0.98$? (Again use Bernoulli's theorem.)

(d) In a certain factory, the percentage of rejects is 2.5%. Use Bernoulli's theorem to find the probability that the deviation from this figure in a sample of 8000 objects will be less than 0.005.

**295.** Fifty objects are chosen (with replacement) from a certain lot. What is the probability that half of those chosen will be of first grade if the probability of choosing a first-grade object is 0.4?

**296.** An observer makes a count of the number of calls people make from a certain phone booth during an interval of time $t$. Find

(a) the probability that he will not witness a single call;

(b) the probability that he will witness exactly two calls; exactly $n$ calls.

**297.** Suppose that on the average $n$ electrons are emitted from a hot cathode per unit of time. What is the probability that exactly $m$ electrons will be emitted from the cathode during an interval $\Delta t$?

**298.** A certain volume $V$ of an ideal gas contains $N$ molecules. Find the mean square deviation of the number of molecules $n$ in a volume $v$ (where $v < V$) from its mean value $\bar{n}$ and the probability $P_N(n)$ that the number of particles in this volume is exactly $n$.

**299.** Suppose that exactly $n$ calls are made through a certain switchboard in an hour. What is the probability that exactly $m$ calls will be made through this switchboard during a specified one-minute interval?

**300.** There are $n$ particles of an impurity in a volume $V$ of a certain liquid. Suppose that we examine a small portion of volume $v$ under a microscope. What will be the probability that this small volume will contain $m$ particles of the impurity?

**301.** Prove the following assertion: For any positive number $\varepsilon$, the probability that a discrete random variable $\xi$ with mathematical expectation $M\xi$ and variance $D\xi$ will deviate from its mathematical expectation by an amount less than $\varepsilon$ is bounded above by the ratio $D\xi/\varepsilon^2$:

$$P(|\xi - M\xi| \geqslant \varepsilon) \leqslant \frac{D\xi}{\varepsilon^2}$$

This is known as Chebyshev's inequality. To what is the probability

$$P(|\xi - M\xi| < \varepsilon).$$

equal?

**302.** The mean length of objects in a certain set is 50 cm and the variance is 0.1. Use Chebyshev's inequality (problem 301) get a bound for the probability that the length of any one of ese objects will lie between 49.5 cm and 50.5 cm.

**303.** Suppose that the probability of the birth of a boy is 515. Use Chebyshev's inequality to obtain a bound for the obability that out of 1000 births, the number of boys will be tween 480 and 550 inclusively.

**304.** Let

$$x_1, x_2, x_3, \ldots, x_n, \ldots$$

a sequence of independent random variables. Suppose that e random variable $x_n$ can assume the values $-n\alpha$, 0, $n\alpha$ with obabilities $1/2n^2$, $1 - 1/n^2$, $1/2n^2$ respectively. Is the law of rge numbers applicable to this sequence of random variables?

**305.** In a set of Bernoulli trials $p = 0.5$. Show that

$$\frac{1}{2\sqrt{n}} \leqslant P_{2n}(n) \leqslant \frac{1}{\sqrt{2n+1}}.$$

**306.** Suppose that $x_1, x_2, \ldots, x_n, \ldots$ are dependent random riables and that

$$\lim_{n\to\infty} \frac{D\left(\sum_{i=1}^{n} x_i\right)}{n^2} = 0,$$

ow that the arithmetic mean of the observed values of these ndom variables converges in probability to the arithmetic ean of their mathematical expectations (Markov's theorem).

# Answers and Directions

**3.** (a) A family of parallel planes; (b) a family of concentric spheres with center at the coordinate origin; (c) a family of hyperboloids of two sheets for $\varphi < 0$; a family of hyperboloids of one sheet for $\varphi > 0$; a cone for $\varphi = 0$.

**8.** In parts (a), (b), and (c), the given points are the extreme values of the corresponding fields.

**9.** The level curves $\varphi =$ const. $> F_1F_2$ are confocal ellipses with foci at $F_1$ and $F_2$. The level curve $\varphi =$ const. $= F_1F_2$ degenerates into the segment $F_1F_2$.

**10.** Ellipsoids of revolution (with axis of revolution passing through the fixed points).

**11.** Circular cylinders for which the fixed straight line is the axis.

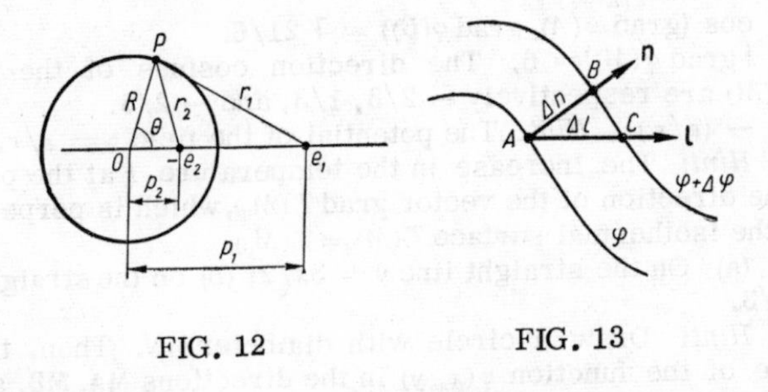


FIG. 12 FIG. 13

**12.** A sphere of radius $R = \sqrt{p_1 p_2}$, where $p_i$ is the distance from the charge $e_i$ (for $i = 1, 2$) to the center of the sphere, which lies on the continuation of the line segment joining the given charges at a point that satisfies the equation

$$\left(\frac{p_1}{p_2} = \frac{e_1^2}{e_2^2}\right)$$

**13.** Yes.

**14.** No.

**15.** 8.6.

**16.** (a) $\left(\frac{\partial f}{\partial x}+\frac{\partial f}{\partial y}\right)\frac{\sqrt{2}}{2}$; (b) $-\frac{\partial f}{\partial x}$.

**17.** 0.

**18.** $\frac{2}{\sqrt{x_0^2+y_0^2}}$.

**19.** $2\sqrt{5}$.

**20.** *Suggestion*: Consider two infinitesimally close level surfaces $\varphi$ and $\varphi+\Delta\varphi$, where $\Delta\varphi>0$ (see Fig. 13). From the drawing, we see that the magnitudes of the displacements in the direction $\mathbf{n}$ from the point $A$ to the point $B$ and in the direction $\mathbf{l}$ from the point $A$ to the point $C$ are connected by the relationship $\Delta n=\Delta l\cos(\mathbf{n}, \mathbf{l})$. Consequently, $\frac{\Delta\varphi}{\Delta l}=\frac{\Delta\varphi}{\Delta n}\cos(\mathbf{n}, \mathbf{l})$. In the limit, this equation gives the desired relationship.

**21.** In the direction of the vector $y_0\mathbf{i}+x_0\mathbf{j}$. The derivative in the direction tangential to the level curve is 0. *Hint*: See problem 20.

**24.** (a) 0; (b) 0; (c) $\mathbf{i}+\mathbf{j}+\mathbf{k}$; (d) 0; (e) $\frac{x\mathbf{j}-y\mathbf{i}}{x^2+y^2}$; (f) $-\mathbf{r}/r^3$.

**25.** $\frac{\partial u}{\partial l}=\frac{\operatorname{grad} u\cdot\operatorname{grad} v}{|\operatorname{grad} v|}$; $\frac{2v}{\sqrt{3}}$.

**26.** $\cos(\operatorname{grad}\varphi(A), \operatorname{grad}\varphi(B))=\sqrt{21}/6$.

**27.** $|\operatorname{grad}\varphi(M)|=6$. The direction cosines of the vector $\operatorname{grad}\varphi(M)$ are respectively $-2/3$, $1/3$, and $-2/3$.

**28.** $-(e/\mathbf{r})r^3$. *Hint*: The potential of the field $\varphi=e/r$.

**29.** *Hint*: The increase in the temperature $T$ at the point $M_0$ is in the direction of the vector $\operatorname{grad} T(M_0)$, which is perpendicular to the isothermal surface $T(M)=T(M_0)$.

**30.** (a) On the straight line $y=3x/2$; (b) on the straight line $y=2x/3$.

**31.** *Hint*: Draw a circle with diameter $MN$. Then, the derivative of the function $\varphi(x, y)$ in the directions **MA, MB**, and **MC** will be respectively $MA_1$, $-MB_1$, and 0.

**32.** *Solution*: The level curve $\varphi(x, y)=0$ is the ellipse $\frac{x^2}{a^2}+\frac{y^2}{b^2}=1$ (see Fig. 14). Since $|\mathbf{r}|+|\mathbf{R}|=2a$ ($r=F_1M$, $R=F_2M$), we have $d|\mathbf{r}|+d|\mathbf{R}|=0$. But $\mathbf{R}=\mathbf{r}+\mathbf{F}_2\mathbf{F}_1$ and $d\mathbf{R}=d\mathbf{r}$. By using the relations $d|\mathbf{R}|=d\mathbf{R}\cdot\mathbf{R}^0$ and $d\mathbf{r}=d\mathbf{r}\cdot\mathbf{r}^0$, we easily obtain $(d\mathbf{r}, \mathbf{r}^0+\mathbf{R}^0)=0$. This means that the vector $\mathbf{r}^0+\mathbf{R}^0$ is perpendicular to the vector $d\mathbf{r}$, which is tangent to the ellipse. Thus, the vector $\mathbf{r}^0+\mathbf{R}^0$ is directed along the outward normal to the level curve $\varphi(x, y)=0$, that is, in the direction of increasing values of the sum $|\mathbf{r}|+|\mathbf{R}|$ and, consequently, of $\operatorname{grad}\varphi(M)=\mathbf{r}^0+\mathbf{R}^0$. The reader should observe how $|\text{grad}\ \varphi(M)|$ varies as the point $M$ is moved around the ellipse.

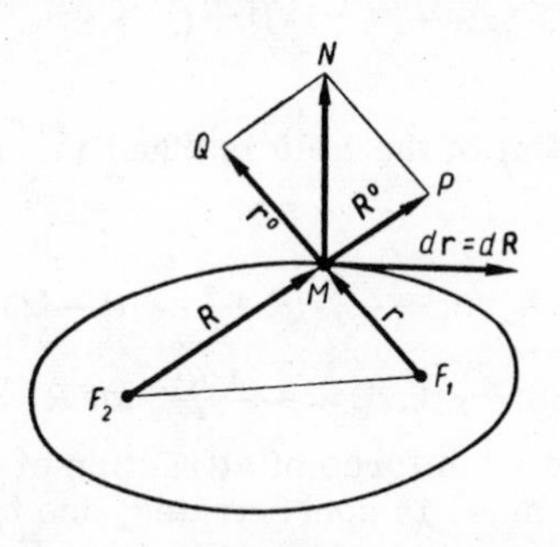


FIG. 14

**33*.** *Solution*: The surface of an ellipsoid of revolution is one of the level surfaces of the scalar field $\varphi(M)=r(P_1, M)+r(P_2, M)\equiv r_1+r_2$. Therefore, $\text{grad}\ \varphi(M)=\text{grad}\ r_1+\text{grad}\ r_2=\frac{\mathbf{r}_1}{r_1}+\frac{\mathbf{r}_2}{r_2}$. From the sum of the unit vectors $\mathbf{r}_1/r_1$ and $\mathbf{r}_2/r_2$ we construct the vector $\text{grad}\ \varphi(M)$ (according to the parallelogram rule). The diagonal of the parallelogram constructed bisects the angle between the sides. Since the vector $\text{grad}\ \varphi(M)$ is orthogonal to the level surface of the function $\varphi(M)$ (cf. the solution of problem 32), it follows that the normal to the ellipsoid at the point $M$ bisects the angle between the rays $P_1M$ and $P_2M$. The assertion of the problem then follows easily.

**34*.** Cf. the solution to problem 33*.

**35.** (a) $\mathbf{r}/r$; (b) $2\mathbf{r}$; (c) $5r^3\mathbf{r}$; (d) $\mathbf{a}$; (e) 0.

**36.** (a) $-2\pi\rho r\mathbf{e}_r\ (r\leqslant a)$ and $-2\pi\rho a^2\frac{\mathbf{e}_r}{r}\ (r\geqslant a)$.

(b) $\mathbf{e}_r-\frac{z}{r}\sin\theta\mathbf{e}_\theta+\cos\theta\mathbf{e}_z$.

(c) $-E_0\cos\theta\left(1+\frac{2R^3}{r^3}\right)\mathbf{e}_r+E_0\left(1-\frac{R^3}{r^3}\right)\sin\theta\mathbf{e}_\theta$.

(d) $-\frac{4}{3}\pi\rho r\mathbf{e}_r$. (e) $-\frac{3(1-3\cos^2\theta)}{r^5}\mathbf{e}_r+\frac{3qa^2\sin 2\theta}{r^4}\mathbf{e}_\theta$.

(f) $-\frac{2\mu\cos\theta}{r^3}\mathbf{e}_r-\frac{\mu\cos\theta}{r^3}\mathbf{e}_\theta$.

**37.** $\text{grad}_{P_0} u=-\int\limits_S \mu(P)\frac{\mathbf{r}_{P_0P}}{r_{P_0P}^2}\,dS_P$.

**38*.** $\text{grad}_{P_0} v=-\iint\limits_{(\omega)} \mu(P)\frac{\mathbf{r}_{P_0P}}{r_{P_0P}^2}\,d\omega_P$.

where

$$\mathbf{r}_{P_0P}=(x_0-x)\,\mathbf{i}+(y_0-y)\,\mathbf{j}.$$

**43.** The potential of the field is equal to $\int_{r_0}^{r} f(r)\,r\,dr+C$, where $r_0=$ const.

**45.** $F_x=F_y=0,\ F_z=\frac{\pi R}{\zeta^2}(R+\zeta-|R-\zeta|)\times\left[\frac{R^2-\zeta^2}{|R^2-\zeta^2|}-1\right]$; for $R>\zeta$, $F_z=0$; for $R<\zeta$, $F_z=-\frac{4\pi R^2}{\zeta^2}$; for $R=\zeta$, $F_z=-2\pi$.

*Hint*: The Newtonian force of attraction of the point $P(\xi,\eta,\zeta)$, at which the unit mass is concentrated, due to the gravitational field caused by a mass continuously distributed on the surface $(S)$ with surface density $\mu(x, y, z)$ is given by the formula

$$\mathbf{F}(P)=F_x(P)\,\mathbf{i}+F_y(P)\,\mathbf{j}+F_z(P)\,\mathbf{k},$$

where

$$F_x=\iint_{(S)}\mu(M)\frac{x-\xi}{r^3}\,dS_M,$$

$$F_y=\iint_{(S)}\mu(M)\frac{y-\eta}{r^3}\,dS_M,$$

$$F_z=\iint_{(S)}\mu(M)\frac{z-\zeta}{r^3}\,dS_M,$$

$$r=r(P,M)=\sqrt{(x-\xi)^2+(y-\eta)^2+(z-\zeta)^2}.$$

**46.** If the $z$-axis is used as the axis of the cylinder and the base is in the $xy$-plane, then

$$F_x=F_y=0,\ F_z=2\pi R\left(\frac{1}{R}-\frac{1}{\sqrt{R^2+h^2}}\right).$$

**47.** If the center of the base of the cone is at the coordinate origin and its axis coincides with the $z$-axis, then

$$F_x=F_y=0,\ F_z=\frac{2\pi}{l}(R+h)-\frac{2\pi Rh}{l^2}\ln\frac{h(l+h)}{R(l-R)},$$

where

$$l=\sqrt{h^2+R^2}.$$

**48.** $\varphi=\frac{2\pi R}{\zeta}(R+\zeta-|R-\zeta|)$. For $R>\zeta$, $\varphi=4\pi R$; for $R<\zeta$, $\varphi=\frac{4\pi R^2}{\zeta}$.

**49.** $kMm/r^2$, where $M$ is the mass of the sphere and $k$ is the gravitational constant.

**50.** $u_l(P_0)=\frac{1}{2}\mu\int_{-l}^{l}\frac{dz}{r_{P_0Q}}=\frac{1}{2}\mu\ln\frac{\sqrt{r_{P_0P}^2+l^2}+l}{\sqrt{r_{P_0P}^2+l^2}-l}$, $\mathbf{F}_l(P_0)=\operatorname{grad}_{P_0}u_l=$

$-\frac{1}{2}\mu\int_{-l}^{l}\frac{\mathbf{r}_{P_0Q}}{r_{P_0Q}^3}dz=\mu\frac{l}{\sqrt{r_{P_0P}^2+l^2}}\cdot\frac{\mathbf{r}_{P_0P}}{r_{P_0P}^2}$, where $Q$ is an arbitrary point on the straight line.

In the case of an infinite line, the desired potential is

$$v=\mu\ln\frac{1}{r_{P_0P}}$$

and the gravitational field strength is grad $v$. To obtain the potential $v$, take the limit of $u_l$ as $l\to\infty$.

**51.** $\mathbf{H}=2I/\rho^2\,(-y\mathbf{i}+x\mathbf{j})$, where $\rho^2=x^2+y^2$. The field lines are given by the equations $x^2+y^2=2c_1$, $z=c_2$.

*Procedure*: Consider a small element $PP_1=d\zeta$ of the $z$-axis (where $OP=\zeta$). According to the Biot-Savart law, the direction of the magnetic field strength $dH$ that will exist at a point $M$ as a result of a current passing through the element $d\zeta$ of the conductor will be perpendicular to the plane defined by the point $M$ and the element $d\zeta$.

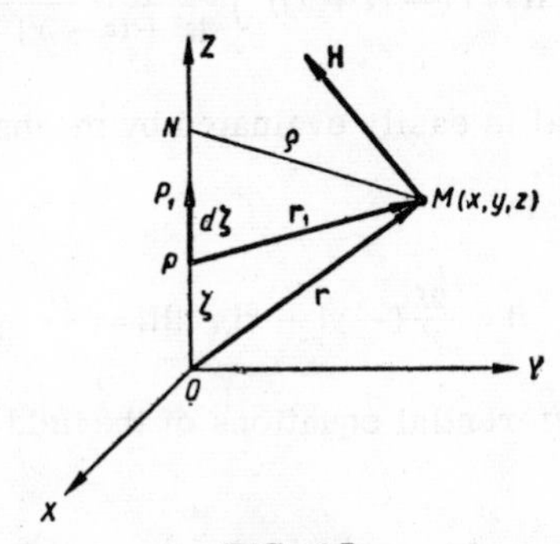


FIG. 15

More specifically, the magnetic field vector will point in a direction such that it will tend to produce a rotation that appears clockwise as viewed from the negative $z$-axis (*whence* the current flows) (see Fig. 15). In other words, the direction of the vector $d\mathbf{H}$ coincides with that of the cross product $d\zeta \times \mathbf{r}_1$, where $d\zeta = \mathbf{PP}_1$ ($|d\zeta| = d\zeta$) and $\mathbf{r}_1 = \mathbf{PM}$. From the same law, the calculated value of the magnetic field intensity is $dH = 1/r_1^2 \sin(d\zeta, \mathbf{r}_1)\, d\zeta$ (where $r_1 = |\mathbf{r}_1|$). Since $|d\zeta \times \mathbf{r}| = \mathbf{r}_1\, d\zeta \sin(d\zeta, \mathbf{r}_1)$, we may write

$$d\mathbf{H} = \frac{1}{r_1^3}(d\zeta \times \mathbf{r}_1)$$

Therefore,

$$\mathbf{H} = \int_{-\infty}^{\infty} \frac{1}{r_1^3}(d\zeta \times \mathbf{r}_1)$$

To evaluate this integral, it is convenient to work with the projections. We have

$$\mathbf{r}_1 = \mathbf{PM} = \mathbf{OM} - \mathbf{OP} = \mathbf{r} - \mathbf{OP} = (x\mathbf{i} + y\mathbf{j} + z\mathbf{k}) - \zeta\mathbf{k} = \\ = x\mathbf{i} + y\mathbf{j} + (z - \zeta)\mathbf{k}$$

and

$$r_1 = \sqrt{x^2 + y^2 + (z - \zeta)^2} = \sqrt{\rho^2 - (z - \zeta)^2},$$

where $\rho = \sqrt{x^2 + y^2}$ is the distance between the point $M$ and the conductor. Therefore, we easily find $d\zeta \times \mathbf{r}_1 = -y\,d\zeta\mathbf{i} + x\,d\zeta\mathbf{j}$ and

$$\mathbf{H} = I(-y\mathbf{i} + x\mathbf{j}) \int_{-\infty}^{\infty} \frac{d\zeta}{[\rho^2 + (z - \zeta)^2]^{3/2}}$$

Here, the integral is easily evaluated by means of the substitution $d = z - \text{ɔ} \tan t$.

We finally obtain

$$\mathbf{H} = \frac{2I}{\rho^2}(-y\mathbf{i} + x\mathbf{j}); \quad |\mathbf{H}| = \frac{2I}{\rho}$$

The system of differential equations of the field lines of the field $\mathbf{H}$ is of the form

$$\frac{dx}{-y} = \frac{dy}{x} = \frac{dz}{0}$$

By integrating this system, we find the family of field lines that we are seeking.

**52*.** $\operatorname{grad}_{P_0} u = -\iiint\limits_{(v)} \rho(P) \frac{\mathbf{r}_{P_0P}}{r^3_{P_0P}}\, dv_P.$

**53.** (a) $x^2 = cy$; (b) $y = c_1 z,\ x^2 + y^2 + z^2 = c_2 y$; (c) $x = c_1 y, y = c_2 z$; (d) the curves of intersection of the hyperbolic cylinder with the parabolic cylinders are of the form $xy = c_1,\ y^2 = c_2 z$; (e) rays issuing from the point at which the charge is placed.

**55.** (a) $(x-c)^2 + y^2 = a^2 + c^2$, where $2a$ is the distance between the wires; (b) $(x^2+y^2)^{3/2} = cx^2$. *Solution*: Since the wires are infinitely long, the field **E** caused by them cannot depend on the coordinate $z$; that is, the field is the same at all points of any straight line $MN$ (see Fig. 16) parallel to the wires: if we draw a plane perpendicular to the wires through an arbitrary point on this straight line, this plane will divide the wires into two infinitely long parts. Thus, the field in question is plane. Suppose that $\mathbf{E} = E_x\mathbf{i} + E_y\mathbf{j}$. Then, the differential equation of the lines of force can be written in the form

$$\frac{dx}{E_x} = \frac{dy}{E_y} \qquad (1)$$

Let us find $E_x$ and $E_y$. As a preliminary to this, we find the potential $\varphi$ of the field. Because of the symmetry referred to above, we may take a point $P$ in the $XY$-plane as our point of observation. Then, the potential caused by the wires at the point $P$ is, because of the principle of superposition of fields,

$$\varphi = \varphi_+ + \varphi_- = e\int_{-\infty}^{\infty} \frac{dz}{R_2} - e\int_{-\infty}^{\infty} \frac{dz}{R_1} =$$
$$= 2e\left(\int_0^{\infty} \frac{dz}{\sqrt{r_2^2 + z^2}} - \int_0^{\infty} \frac{dz}{\sqrt{r_1^2 + z^2}}\right)$$

If we integrate, we obtain $\varphi = 2e(\ln r_2 - \ln r_1)$. Also, if we start with the relation $\mathbf{E} = -\operatorname{grad}\varphi$, we find

$$\mathbf{E} = \frac{2e}{r_2^2}\mathbf{r}_2 - \frac{2e}{r_1^2}\mathbf{r}_1$$

If we denote the distance between the wires by $L = 2a$, so that the coordinates of the points $A$ and $B$ are respectively $(0, -a, 0)$ and $(0, a, 0)$, we have

$$\mathbf{r}_1 = x\mathbf{i} + (y+a)\mathbf{j}, \mathbf{r}_2 = x\mathbf{i} + (y-a)\mathbf{j}$$

and

$$E_x = \frac{8eaxy}{r_1^2 r_2^2},\ E_y = -\frac{4ea}{r_1^2 r_2^2}(x^2 - y^2 + a^2)$$

The differential equation of the lines of force (1) becomes, after we substitute the values found for $E_x$ and $E_y$,

$$[x^2-(y^2-a^2)]\,dx+2xy\,dy=0$$

If we now set $y^2-a^2=u^2$, we obtain the homogeneous equation $(x^2-u^2)\,dx+2xu\,du=0$. When we solve this equation and return to the original variables, we obtain the desired equation of the lines of force of this field: $(x-c)^2+y^2=a^2+c^2$.

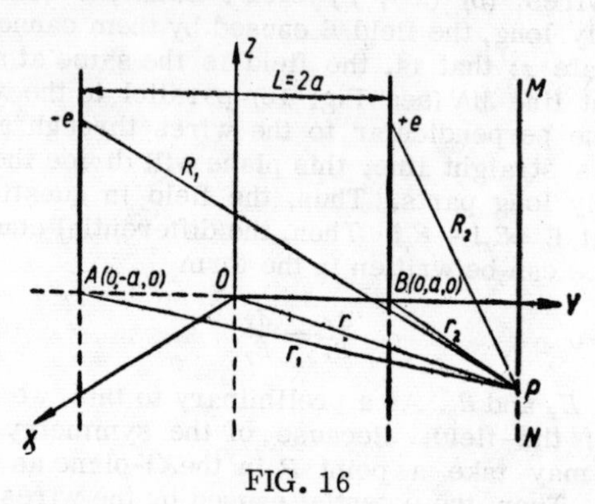


FIG. 16

**57.** $r=c\sin^2\theta$, $\varphi=$ const. *Hint*: Use the assertion in problem 56b.

**62.** (a) The trajectories are the lines $y=$ const.; the motion proceeds in the direction of the positive $x$-axis with velocity equal to 1. (b) The trajectories constitute a family of circles passing through the coordinate origin with centers on the $y$-axis. The fluid streams out from the coordinate origin to the left and into the coordinate origin from the right (see Fig. 17) with velocity

$$v=\sqrt{\left(\frac{\partial\varphi}{\partial x}\right)^2+\left(\frac{\partial\varphi}{\partial y}\right)^2}=\frac{1}{x^2+y^2}$$

(c) The trajectories are the curves $y-\dfrac{y}{x^2+y^2}=$ const. The velocity is

$$\mathbf{v}=-\left(1+\frac{y^2-x^2}{(x^2+y^2)^2}\right)\mathbf{i}+\frac{2xy}{(x^2+y^2)^2}\mathbf{j}$$

**63.** (1) 0; (2) $\pi a^2$; (3) $1/6\,(2+\sqrt{3})$; (4) $\pi/6\,[(1+4a^2)^{3/2}-1]$; (5) (a) $2\pi R^7/105$; (b) $-\,2\pi R^7/105$; (6) 0; (7) 2/15; (8) $\pi Rr^2$; (9) $R^2H\,(2/3\,R+\pi H/8)$.

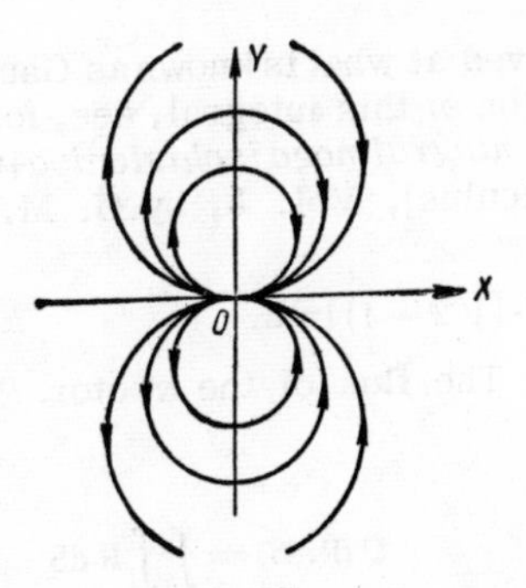


FIG. 17

**64.** (1) $I=2\iiint\limits_{(\omega)}(x+y+z)\,d\omega$; (2) 0.

**65.** *Solution*: $Q(\mathbf{v}; S)=Q(\mathbf{r}; S)=\iint\limits_S r_n\,dS=\iint\limits_S(x\cos\alpha+y\cos\beta+z\cos\gamma)\,dS=3T$, where $\mathbf{v}=\mathbf{r}=x\mathbf{i}+y\mathbf{j}+z\mathbf{k}$, $r_n=\mathbf{r}\cdot\mathbf{n}$, where in turn $\mathbf{n}=\cos\alpha\mathbf{i}+\cos\beta\mathbf{j}+\cos\gamma\mathbf{k}$ is the unit outer normal vector to the surface $S$ of the body $(T)$.

**66.** (a) $\pi R^2H$; (b) $3\pi R^2H$; (c) $4\pi R^3$.

**67.** $(\pi+2)/3$.

**68.** $Q=0$, if the body $(G)$ does not contain the coordinate origin. If it does contain the coordinate origin, $Q=-4\pi$. *Procedure*: Let $\mathbf{r}=x\mathbf{i}+y\mathbf{j}+z\mathbf{k}$ denote the velocity of a particle of the liquid $\mathbf{v}=\frac{1}{r^2}\times\frac{\mathbf{r}}{r}=\frac{\mathbf{r}}{r^3}$. Let $\mathbf{n}=\cos\alpha\mathbf{i}+\cos\beta\mathbf{j}+\cos\gamma\mathbf{k}$ denote the outer normal to the surface $S$ of the body $(G)$. Then, the amount of liquid is given by

$$Q=Q(\mathbf{v}; S)=\iint\limits_{(S)}v_n\,dS=$$

$$=\iint\limits_{(S)}\frac{1}{r^3}(x\cos\alpha+y\cos\beta+z\cos\gamma)\,dS$$

Obviously, the direction cosines of the vector $\mathbf{r}$ are

$$\cos\alpha'=\frac{x}{r},\quad \cos\beta'=\frac{y}{r},\quad \cos\gamma'=\frac{z}{r}.$$

Therefore

$$Q=\iint\limits_{(S)}\frac{1}{r^2}(\cos\alpha\cos\alpha'+\cos\beta\cos\beta'+\cos\gamma\cos\gamma')\,dS=$$

$$=\iint\limits_{(S)}\frac{\cos(\mathbf{n},\mathbf{r})}{r^2}\,dS$$

and we have arrived at what is known as Gauss' surface integral. (For the evaluation of this integral, see, for example, *Kurs differentsial'nogo i integral'nogo ischisleniya* [Course in differential and integral calculus], Vol. 3, by G. M. Fikhtengol'ts, 1949, p. 409).

69. $\frac{3-\sqrt{3}}{2}+(\sqrt{2}-1)\ln 2.$

70. *Solution*: The flux of the vector $R$ through the surface $S$ is

$$Q(\mathbf{R}, S)=\iint\limits_{(S)} \mathbf{R}\, d\mathbf{S}$$

where $d\mathbf{S}$ is a vector directed along the normal to a surface element $dS$ and equal in magnitude to the area of that element. We may represent this flux as the limit of the corresponding approximating sum

$$Q(\mathbf{R}, S)=\lim_{\max d(\Delta S_i)\to 0} \sum_{(i)} \mathbf{R}_i \Delta\mathbf{S}_i$$

where $d(\Delta S_i)$ is the diameter of the element $dS_i$. In the scalar product $\mathbf{R}_i\Delta\mathbf{S}_i=R_i\Delta S_i \cos(\mathbf{R}_i, \Delta\mathbf{S}_i)$, the factor $\Delta S_i \cos(\mathbf{R}_i, \Delta\mathbf{S}_i)$ represents the projection of the element $\Delta S_i$ in the direction perpendicular to the vector $\mathbf{R}_i$:

$$\Delta S_i \cos(\mathbf{R}_i, \Delta\mathbf{S}_i)=\Delta\mathbf{S}_i\mathbf{n}=(\Delta S_i)_n \qquad (|\mathbf{n}|=1)$$

Through an area $(\Delta S_i)_n$ there pass $N_i=k|\mathbf{R}_i|(\Delta S_i)_n$ field lines. Therefore,

$$\mathbf{R}_i\,\Delta\mathbf{S}_i=|\mathbf{R}_i|(\Delta S_i)_n=\frac{N_i}{k}$$

and

$$Q(\mathbf{R}, S)=\lim_{d(\Delta S_i)\to 0}\sum_i \mathbf{R}_i\Delta\mathbf{S}_i=\frac{1}{k}N$$

where $N$ is the number of field lines crossing the surface $S$.

71. (a) The flux is equal to $-4\pi q$ if the charge $q$ lies within the sphere and it is equal to zero if it lies outside. This result holds for an arbitrary closed surface—a consequence of the fact that the flux of an arbitrary vector $\mathbf{a}$ is independent of the shape of the surface, which is a consequence of the Gauss-Ostrogradskiy

theorem. Let us prove this. Suppose that there is an isolated source of a field a at a point $P$ enclosed by an arbitrary surface $S$. Consider the region $(v)$ bounded by the two surfaces $S$ and $S_1$, where $S_1$ lies inside $S$ (see Fig. 18). Within this region, div a $= 0$. It follows from the Gauss-Ostrogradskiy theorem that

$$\iint_{(S)} a_n\, dS + \iint_{S_1} a_{n_1}\, dS = 0.$$

Here, the projections of the vector a are taken on the outer normals to the surfaces in question. If we reverse the direction of the outer normal to the surface $S_1$, the projection will change its sign and we will obtain

$$\iint_{S} a_n\, dS = \iint_{S_1} a_{n_1}\, dS, \text{ т. е. } Q(\mathbf{a};\, S) = Q(\mathbf{a};\, S_1).$$

This equation may be interpreted as follows: The flux of the vector through a closed surface remains unchanged as a result of deformation of that surface so long as this surface does not touch new sources or sinks (where div a $\neq 0$). Therefore, it follows in particular that in a solenoidal field a (where div a $= 0$) the same number of field lines will pass through all sections of a vector tube (see problem 70); that is, in such a field, the field lines neither appear nor disappear but either go out to infinity or form closed curves.

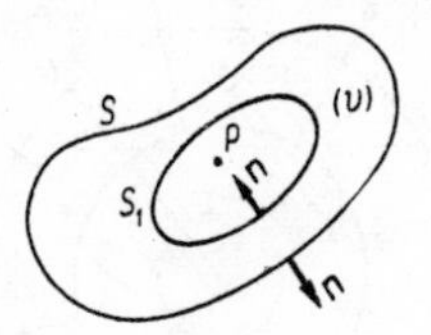


FIG. 18

**72.** *Solution*: Let us construct a spherical surface $S$ through the point in question. Then,

$$Q(\mathbf{D};\, S) = \iint_{(S)} D_n\, dS = \iint_{(S)} D \cos(\mathbf{D},\, \mathbf{a})\, dS.$$

From the Gauss-Ostrogradskiy theorem (problem 71),

$$\iint_{(S)} D \cos(\mathbf{D},\, \mathbf{a})\, dS = 4\pi\Sigma q.$$

Because of the symmetry of the situation, the vector D must have the same value at all points of the spherical surface and, since $\cos(\mathbf{D}, \mathbf{a}) = 1$, it follows from the preceding equation that

$$D \cdot 4\pi r^2 = 4\pi \Sigma q$$

and

$$D = \frac{\Sigma q}{r^2}, \quad \mathbf{D} = \frac{\Sigma q}{r^3}\,\mathbf{r},$$

where $r$ is the distance from the point in question to the center of the sphere (which we may assume to be at the coordinate origin). Therefore, we note that if the point in question lies inside the charged sphere (where $r < a$) (see Fig. 19), there will be no charges within the sphere of radius $r$, so that $\Sigma q = 0$ and $D = 0$. On the other hand, if the point in question lies outside the sphere $S$, this sphere of radius $r$ will enclose the sphere of radius $a$. Therefore, it will enclose a charge $q$. In this case,

$$\Sigma q = q = \sigma \cdot 4\pi a^2$$

and

$$D = \frac{\Sigma q}{r^2} = \frac{q}{r^2} = 4\pi \frac{a^2}{r^2}\sigma, \quad \mathbf{D} = \frac{4\pi a^2 \sigma}{r^3}\,\mathbf{r} \quad (r > a).$$

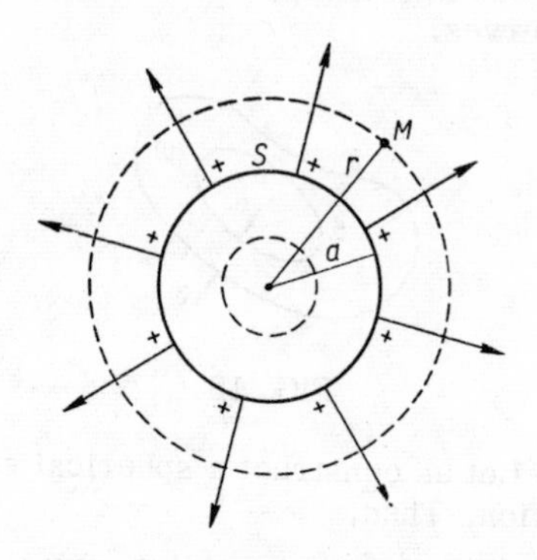


FIG. 19

**73.** *Solution*: Let us draw a cylindrical surface $S_0$ (see Fig. 20) of altitude $h$ through the point in question. And let us form a closed cylinder by drawing plane surfaces $S_1$ and $S_2$ through the top and bottom of this cylindrical surface. Because of the symmetry of the situation, the vector $\mathbf{D}$ is directed perpendicularly to the lateral surface $S_0$ and must be of the same magnitude at all points of it. From this it follows that the flux through the surfaces $S_1$ and $S_2$ is 0. From Ostrogradskiy's theorem,

$$\iint\limits_{S_0+S_1+S_2} D_n\,dS = \iint\limits_{S_0} D\,dS = D\cdot 2\pi rh = 4\pi\Sigma q.$$

A charge $\Sigma q$ enclosed by the combined surface $S_0+S_1+S_2$ is distributed on a cylinder of radius $a$ and altitude $h$ and is equal to $\Sigma q = 2\pi ah\sigma$. From this, we find

$$D = 4\pi\,\frac{2\pi ah\sigma}{2\pi rh} = \frac{4\pi a\sigma}{r};\quad \mathbf{D} = \frac{4\pi a\sigma}{r^2}\,\mathbf{r} \quad (r > a).$$

By a procedure analogous to that followed in solving problem 72, we can verify that the field within the charged cylinder is equal to zero.

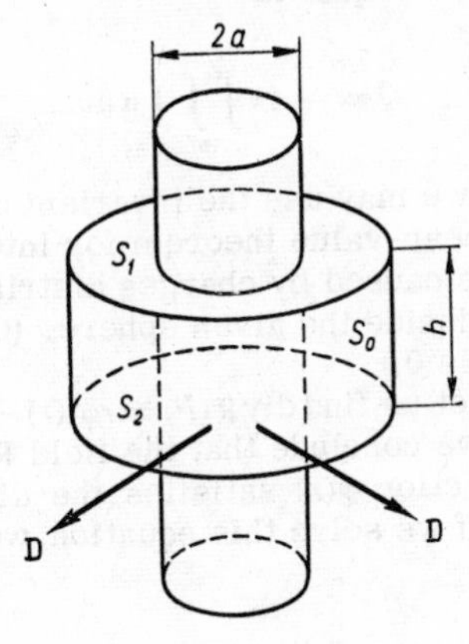


FIG. 20

**74.** $\dfrac{4\pi\gamma mr^2h}{\sqrt{r^2+h^2}}$, where $\gamma$ is the universal gravitational constant.

**75.** $2\pi\sigma$.

**76.** $Q(\mathbf{a};\,S) = \iint\limits_{(S)} (\pm a_r)\,r\,d\varphi\,dz.$

**78.** 6.

**79.** 0.

**80.** (a) 2; (b) 3.

**81.** (a) At the point $P_1$, there is a source of density $7/4\pi$; at the point $P_2$, there is a sink of density $1/4\pi$; at the point $P_3$ there is neither a source nor a sink.

**82.** div $\mathbf{R} = 3f(r) - rf'(r)$.

**83.** *Method of solution*: The scalar field defined by the equation $\varphi =$ div $\mathbf{R}$ is called the source field belonging to the vector field $\mathbf{R}$. The total strength of the sources of the field $\mathbf{R}$ that lie within a closed surface bounding a region $(G)$ is equal to the integral $\iiint\limits_{(G)} \operatorname{div} \mathbf{R}\, dv$.

**84.** The divergence of both fields is zero. *Procedure*: Assuming that the axis of rotation of the liquid coincides with the $Z$-axis and that $\mathbf{r}$ is the radius-vector of the revolving point $M(x, y, z)$, we find $\mathbf{v} = \boldsymbol{\omega} \times \mathbf{r}$, where $\boldsymbol{\omega} = \omega\mathbf{k}$ is the angular velocity. From this, we easily obtain $\mathbf{v} = \omega(-y\mathbf{i} + x\mathbf{j})$, where $\omega = |\boldsymbol{\omega}|$.

**86.** *Hint*: Cf. the answer to problem 71.

**87.** *Hint for part (b)*: Since the flux of the vector $\mathbf{F}$ from within the region $(v)$ is equal to

$$Q = -4\pi \iiint\limits_{(v)} \mu\, dv,$$

to compute div $\mathbf{F}$, we may use the invariant definition of the divergence and the mean-value theorem for integrals.

**88.** The field is caused by charges distributed with constant density $\rho = 3l/4\pi$ inside the given sphere. (Outside the sphere, the charge density is 0.)

**89.** *Solution*: Let us find div $\mathbf{R}(P) = r\varphi'(r) + 3\varphi(r)$, where $\varphi(r) = f(r)/r$. From this, we conclude that the field $\mathbf{R}$ will be solenoidal only when the function $\varphi(r)$ satisfies the differential equation $r\varphi'(r) + 3\varphi(r) = 0$. If we solve this equation, we obtain $\varphi(r) = c/r^3$. Consequently,

$$|\mathbf{R}| = |f(r)| = \frac{|c|}{r^2}.$$

**90.** (a) $3rz$; (b) $\frac{1}{r^2}\frac{\partial}{\partial r}(r^2 a_r)$; (c) $\frac{2\cos\theta}{r}$; (d) 0; (e) 0.

**92.** (a) $2\pi$; (b) $-4\pi a^2\sqrt{3}$; (c) $\Gamma = 0$ if the coordinate origin is outside the circle and $\Gamma = 2\pi$ if the coordinate origin is within the circle $(C)$; (d) 0; (e) $-3\pi R^2/16$; (f) 0; (g) $2\pi\sqrt{2}R^2 \sin(\pi/4 - \alpha)$; (h) 0. If the vectors in the condition of the problem are thought of as a distribution of forces applied to the contour, the inequality $\Gamma > 0$ means that the contour will rotate in the positive direction. If $\Gamma < 0$, the contour rotates in the negative direction.

**93.** (a) If the circle lies in the $XY$-plane, the circulation $\Gamma$ of the vector $\mathbf{a}$ will be $-\pi b^2$. If the circle lies in the plane $y = b$, then $\Gamma = 0$.

(b) $w_{\mathbf{k}}(P_0) = \lim_{C \to P_0} \left\{ \frac{1}{S_C} \int_C \mathbf{a}\, d\mathbf{r} \right\} = -1.$

**94.** $\Gamma = \int_L \mathbf{H}\, d\mathbf{r} = 4\pi I$; 0.

**95.** (a) 0; (b) 0.

**96.** The assertion that the flux of the curl is independent of the shape of the surface follows immediately from Stokes' theorem:

$$\int_L \mathbf{a}\, d\mathbf{L} = \iint_{(S)} \operatorname{curl} \mathbf{a}\, d\mathbf{S}$$

(Cf. answer to problem 71a).

**97.** *Hint*: Derive the formula $\omega = 1/2 \operatorname{curl} \mathbf{v} \cdot \mathbf{l}$.

**99.** *Hint*: Cf. problem 97 and the hint to it.

**100.** *Hint*: The assertion in the problem is a specific case of Stokes' theorem (as applied to the magnetic field vector).

**101.** $\operatorname{curl} \mathbf{R}(P) = [\rho\varphi'(\rho) + 2\varphi(\rho)]\, \mathbf{k}$, where $\varphi(\rho) = f(\rho)/\rho$.

*Solution*: It is convenient to write the vector $\mathbf{R}(P)$ in the form

$$\mathbf{R}(P) = f(\rho)\, \frac{\mathbf{t}(P)}{\rho} = \varphi(\rho)\, \mathbf{t}(P),$$

where $\varphi(\rho) = f(\rho)/\rho$, and $\mathbf{t}(P)$ is a vector collinear with $\tau(P)$ and of length $\rho$. We direct the $Z$-axis along the straight line $l$ and the $X$- and $Y$-axes in a plane perpendicular to it. We denote the coordinates of the point $P$ by $x$, $y$, and $z$. Then, the components of the vector $\mathbf{t}(P)$ will be $-y, x, 0$ and the components of the vector $\mathbf{R}(P)$ will be

$$R_x(P) = -y\varphi(\rho); \quad R_y(P) = x\varphi(\rho); \quad R_z(P) = 0.$$

Therefore,

$$\frac{\partial R_x(P)}{\partial y} = -y\varphi'(\rho)\, \frac{\partial \rho}{\partial y} - \varphi(\rho)$$

or, since

$$\rho^2 = x^2 + y^2 \text{ and } 2\rho\frac{\partial \rho}{\partial y} = 2y, \quad \frac{\partial \rho}{\partial y} = \frac{y}{\rho},$$

we have

$$\frac{\partial R_x(P)}{\partial y} = -\frac{y^2}{\rho}\, \varphi'(\rho) - \varphi(\rho).$$

Analogously,

$$\frac{\partial R_y(P)}{\partial x} = \frac{x^2}{\rho}\varphi'(\rho) + \varphi(\rho).$$

Also, obviously,

$$\frac{\partial R_x}{\partial z} = \frac{\partial R_y}{\partial z} = 0.$$

Finally, by using the formula given in problem 95 for curl R $(P)$ we obtain the desired result.

**102.** The length of the vector R $(P)$ must be inversely proportional to the distance $\rho$.

*Hint*: Use the result of the solution of problem 101.

**103.** *Solution*: For simplicity, let us consider the field of a direct current $I$. The circulation of the vector **H** around a curve can be represented in the form

$$\Gamma = \int_l (\mathbf{H}, \boldsymbol{\tau})\, ds = \int_{abcda} (\mathbf{H}, d\mathbf{l}), \qquad (l = abcda),$$

where

$$d\mathbf{l} = \boldsymbol{\tau}\, dS.$$

We represent the vector denoting the displacement of a point in the form (Fig. 21a)

$$d\mathbf{l} = d\mathbf{l}_\varphi + d\mathbf{l}_r,$$

where $d\mathbf{l}_\varphi$ is directed along the tangent to a line of force, which, in the present case, is a circle with center on the axis of the current and $d\mathbf{l}_r$ is a vector directed along the normal to the line of force or to the vector **H**.

Obviously,

$$(\mathbf{H}, d\mathbf{l}) = (\mathbf{H}, d\mathbf{l}_\varphi + d\mathbf{l}_r) = (\mathbf{H}, d\mathbf{l}_\varphi).$$

But $dl_\varphi = ds = r\, d\varphi$ and $H = 2I/cr$. This formula is obtained from the Biot-Savart law. Therefore,

$$(\mathbf{H}, d\mathbf{l}) = \frac{2I}{c}\, d\varphi.$$

Consequently,

$$\Gamma = \frac{4\pi I}{c}.$$

We note that this formula is valid for an arbitrary relative position of the curve *abcda* with respect to the conductor; that is, it applies both when the curve *abcda* encircles the conductor and when it does not. If the curve *abcda* does not encircle the conductor (Fig. 21b),

$$\Gamma = \int\limits_{abcda} (\mathbf{H},\ d\mathbf{l}) = \int\limits_{abc} (\mathbf{H},\ d\mathbf{l}) + \int\limits_{cda} (\mathbf{H},\ d\mathbf{l}).$$

But since

$$\int\limits_{abc} (\mathbf{H},\ d\mathbf{l}) = \frac{2I}{c}(\varphi_2 - \varphi_1)$$

and

$$\int\limits_{cda} (\mathbf{H},\ d\mathbf{l}) = \frac{2I}{c}(\varphi_1 - \varphi_2),$$

we finally obtain $\Gamma = 0$.

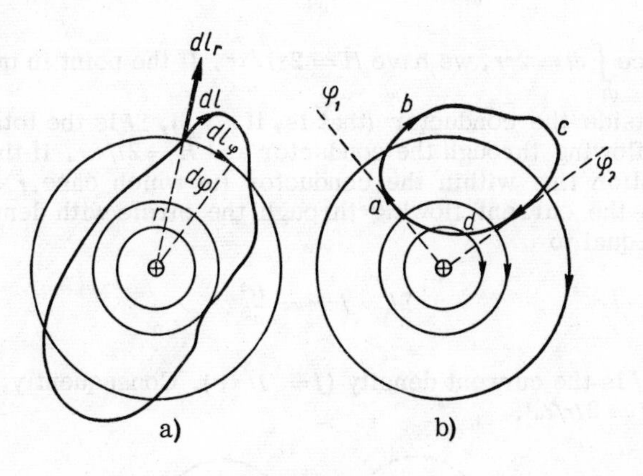


FIG. 21

**104.** $\omega(P) = -z\mathbf{j}$.
Hint: $\omega(P) = 1/2$ curl $\mathbf{v}$ (see problem 99).
**105.** *Hint*: It will be sufficient to show that div curl $\mathbf{R} = 0$.
**106.** *Hint*: The problem consists in showing that

$$\iint\limits_{(S)} \operatorname{curl}_n \mathbf{R}\, dS = 0.$$

Use Ostrogradskiy's theorem and the assertion of problem 105.

**107.** 0. Cf. the hint to problem 83.

**108.** $Q = \iint\limits_{(S)} \operatorname{div} \mathbf{v}\, dS = \iint\limits_{(S)} \left(\frac{\partial u}{\partial x} + \frac{\partial v}{\partial y}\right) dx\, dy;$

$$\Gamma = \iint\limits_{(S)} \left(\frac{\partial v}{\partial x} - \frac{\partial u}{\partial y}\right) dx\, dy.$$

**110.** *Solution*: It follows from the symmetry of the problem that the magnetic field intensity is the same at all points equidistant from the axis and that it is directed tangentially to a circle with center on the axis of the conductor. To solve the problem, we use the assertion in problem 100. As our curve $l$, we take a magnetic line of force (see Fig. 22). Then, the circulation of the vector $\mathbf{H}$ will be

$$\int\limits_{(l)} (\mathbf{H},\, d\mathbf{l}) = H \int\limits_{(l)} dl = \frac{4\pi}{c} \Sigma I,$$

or, since $\int\limits_{(l)} dl = 2\pi r$, we have $H = 2\Sigma I / cr$. If the point in question lies outside the conductor (that is, if $r > a$), $\Sigma I$ is the total current $I$ flowing through the conductor and $H = 2I/cr$. If the point in question lies within the conductor (in which case, $r < a$), $\Sigma I$ denotes the current flowing through the circle with density $\pi r^2$, and is equal to

$$\Sigma I = j\pi r^2 = \frac{Ir^2}{a^2},$$

where $j$ is the current density ($j = I/\pi a^2$). Consequently, in this case, $H = 2Ir/ca^2$.

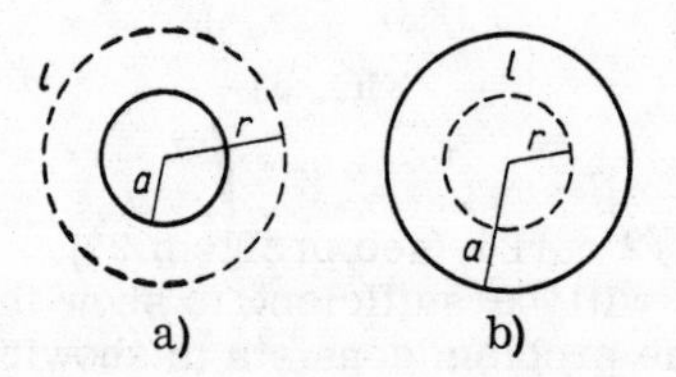


FIG. 22

**111.** The field outside the tube is $H_{\text{ext}} = 2I/cr$; the field inside the tube is 0.

**112.** *Solution*: According to assertion of problem 100,

$$\int_{(l)} (\mathbf{H},\ d\mathbf{l}) = \frac{4\pi}{c}\ \Sigma I,$$

where $(l)$ is an arbitrary closed contour in the magnetic field in question. In the expression above, $\Sigma I$ represents the algebraic sum of the currents threading the contour. If a surface $S$ is drawn over the contour $(l)$ (that is, if $(l)$ is the boundary of the surface $S$), all these currents pass through $S$. Therefore, $\Sigma I$ can be represented as the integral of the current density through the surface

$$\Sigma I = \iint_{(S)} \mathbf{j}\ d\mathbf{S},$$

where $d\mathbf{S}$ is an area vector, that is, a vector directed perpendicularly to the surface and equal in magnitude to the area. Thus,

$$\int_{(l)} (\mathbf{H},\ d\mathbf{l}) = \iint_{(S)} \frac{4\pi}{c}\mathbf{j}\ d\mathbf{S}.$$

But, from Stokes' theorem,

$$\int_{(l)} \mathbf{H}\ d\mathbf{l} = \iint_{(S)} \text{curl}\ \mathbf{H}\ d\mathbf{S}.$$

Therefore, for an arbitrary surface $S$,

$$\iint_{(S)} \text{curl}\ \mathbf{H}\ d\mathbf{S} = \iint_{(S)} \frac{4\pi}{c}\ \mathbf{j}\ dS.$$

From this we get

$$\text{curl}\ \mathbf{H} = \frac{4\pi}{c}\ \mathbf{j}.$$

This equation is the differential form of the circulation theorem formulated in problem 100.

Equation (2) expresses the fact that the divergence of the magnetic flux density vector $\mathbf{B} = \mu\mathbf{H}$ of a constant magnetic field is 0.

**114.** As an example, let us consider the solution of the problem for the field $\mathbf{H} = 2I/r^2\,(x\mathbf{j} - y\mathbf{i})$, where $r^2 = x^2 + y^2$. If we use, for example, the formula given in problem 95, we easily find that curl $\mathbf{H} = 0$. Consequently, the field $\mathbf{H}$ has a potential (see problem 113) and therefore, $\mathbf{H} = \text{grad}\ \varphi$ (where $\varphi$ is the potential of the field $\mathbf{H}$). Furthermore,

$$\mathbf{H}\,d\mathbf{r} = 2I\,\frac{x\mathbf{j} - y\mathbf{i}}{x^2 + y^2}(\mathbf{i}\,dx + \mathbf{j}\,dy + \mathbf{k}\,dz) =$$

$$= 2I\,\frac{x\,dy - y\,dx}{x^2 + y^2} = 2Id\left(\arctan\frac{y}{x} + C\right).$$

Therefore (see problem 35), we conclude that the desired potential is

$$\varphi = 2I\left(\arctan\frac{y}{x} + C\right).$$

**115.** (a) $\text{curl}\ \mathbf{a} = \left(\frac{\partial a_r}{\partial z} - \frac{\partial a_z}{\partial r}\right)\mathbf{e}_\varphi$, $\text{curl}\ \mathbf{b} = (r^2 + z^2)\,\mathbf{e}_\varphi$;

(b) $\text{curl}\ \mathbf{a} = \frac{1}{r\sin\theta}\frac{\partial a_r}{\partial\varphi}\mathbf{e}_\theta - \frac{1}{r}\frac{\partial a_r}{\partial\theta}\mathbf{e}_\varphi$;

(c) $\text{curl}\ \mathbf{a} = z\mathbf{e}_\varphi + \frac{\cos\varphi}{r}\mathbf{e}_z$;

(d) $\text{curl}\ \mathbf{a} = \frac{\sin\theta}{r^2}\mathbf{e}_\varphi$;

(e) 0.

**117.** The Laplacians of all these functions are equal to zero (in the first two expressions, we assume that $r \neq 0$).

**118.**

$$\mathbf{E} = \iiint\limits_{(v)} \rho\,\frac{\mathbf{r}}{\varepsilon r^3}\,dv.$$

**119.** *Hint*: If we assume that there exist two vectors $\mathbf{a}_1$ and $\mathbf{a}_2$ satisfying equations (1) and the boundary condition (2), we obtain the boundary-value problem

$$\text{div}\ \mathbf{b} = 0, \quad \text{curl}\ \mathbf{b} = 0,$$
$$b_n = 0.$$

for the vector $\mathbf{b} = \mathbf{a}_1 - \mathbf{a}_2$. From this it follows that the vector $\mathbf{b}$ has a potential: $\mathbf{b} = \text{grad}\ \varphi$; therefore, $\text{div grad}\ \varphi = \Delta\varphi = 0$. Green's formula can then be used if we set $u = v = \varphi$.

**120.** *Hint*: Set $\varphi = 1$ and $\psi = u^2$ in the second of Green's formulas.

**121.** In the case of cylindrical coordinates, $u = c_1 \ln r + c_2$; in the case of spherical coordinates, $u = c_1/r + c_2$.

**122.** Ostrogradskiy's formula for the vector grad $\varphi$ is of the form

$$\iiint\limits_{(T)} \Delta\varphi\,dT = \iint\limits_{S} \frac{\partial\varphi}{\partial n}\,dS. \qquad (1)$$

The integral $\iint\limits_{(S)} \frac{\partial \varphi}{\partial n}\, dS$ is equal to the flux of the vector **v** (that is, the amount of liquid flowing through the surface $S$ in a unit of time). Since $\mathbf{v} = \text{grad}\, \varphi$, we have $\Delta\varphi = \text{div}\, \mathbf{v}$. Equation (1) shows that the integral of the divergence of the vector **v** over the volume $T$ occupied by the liquid is equal to the flux of this vector through the boundary of the region $T$. If the liquid is incompressible (in which case $\text{div}\, \mathbf{v} = 0$), this flux will be equal to zero.

**125.** No.

**126.** *Solution*: By definition, the vector potential of the magnetic field of a linear current is

$$\mathbf{A} = \frac{I}{c} \int_{-\infty}^{\infty} \frac{d\mathbf{l}}{R}.$$

Because of the symmetry of the situation, the field will be the same in all planes perpendicular to the $Z$-axis (see Fig. 23); therefore, we may take our point of observation $P$ on the $XY$-plane. Obviously, $A_x = A_y = 0$ and

$$A_z = \frac{I}{c} \int_{-\infty}^{\infty} \frac{dz}{\sqrt{r^2 + z^2}} = \frac{I}{c} \lim_{N\to\infty} \int_{-N}^{N} \frac{dz}{\sqrt{r^2 + z^2}} =$$

$$= \frac{2I}{c} \lim_{N\to\infty} \left[\ln\left(N + \sqrt{N^2 + x^2 + y^2}\right) - \ln r\right].$$

Also,

$$\mathbf{H} = H_x \mathbf{i} + H_y \mathbf{j} = \left(\frac{\partial A_z}{\partial y}\, \mathbf{i} - \frac{\partial A_z}{\partial x}\, \mathbf{j}\right)_{N=\infty},$$

so that

$$H_x = \left.\frac{\partial A_z}{\partial y}\right|_{N=\infty} = -\frac{2I}{cr^2}\, y; \quad H_y = -\left.\frac{\partial A_z}{\partial x}\right|_{N=\infty} = \frac{2I}{cr^2}\, x.$$

Consequently,

$$\mathbf{H} = -\frac{2I}{cr^2}\, y\mathbf{i} + \frac{2I}{cr^2}\, x\mathbf{j}, \quad H = |\mathbf{H}| = \sqrt{H_x^2 + H_y^2} = \frac{2I}{cr}.$$

As the final expression for the vector **H** shows, the logarithmic divergence of the vector **A** has no significance. Therefore, the logarithmically divergent term $\ln\left(N + \sqrt{N^2 + x^2 + y^2}\right)$ in the expression $A_z$ can be discarded. (The vector **A** has no actual physical meaning but the vector **H** represents forces acting in a magnetic field on moving charges and conductors.) Therefore, the desired potential **A** can be represented in the form $\mathbf{A} = A_z\mathbf{k} = -2I/c \ln r \cdot \mathbf{k}$.

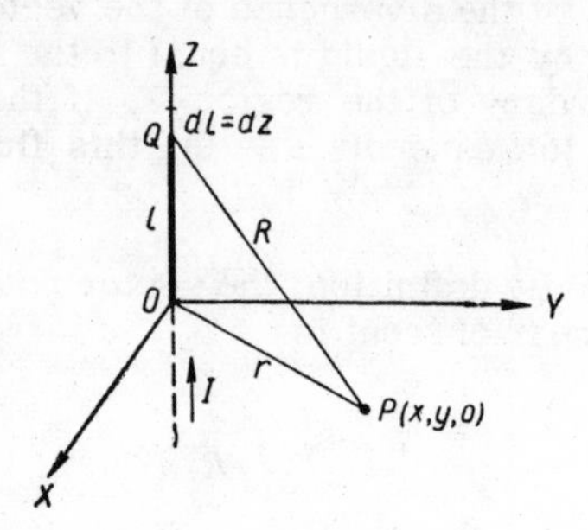


FIG. 23

**127.** $\mathbf{A} = -I/c\ [\mathbf{i} \ln(r-x) + \mathbf{j} \ln(r-y) + \mathbf{k} \ln(r-z)]$, where $r^2 = x^2 + y^2 + z^2$. (In the expressions for the projections of the vector **A**, the terms that are logarithmically divergent at infinity and which do not contribute in the evaluation of the field intensity are discarded. Cf. the solution to problem 126.)

**128.**

$$\mathbf{H} = \frac{3(\boldsymbol{\mu}, \mathbf{R})\mathbf{R}}{R^5} - \frac{\boldsymbol{\mu}}{R^3}.$$

**129.**

$$u = \begin{cases} 2\pi\mu\left(R^2 - \dfrac{r^2}{3}\right) & (r \leqslant R) \\ \dfrac{e}{r} & (r \geqslant R), \end{cases}$$

where $\mu$ is the volume charge density:

$$\mu = \begin{cases} \rho = \text{const.} & \text{for} \quad r < R, \\ 0 & \text{for} \quad r > R. \end{cases}$$

*Solution*: The problem reduces to integrating Poisson's equation $\Delta u = -4\pi\mu$. Because of the spherically symmetric charge distribution (note that the potential $u$ depends only on the distance $r$), in spherical coordinates (with origin at the center of the sphere) the equation becomes

$$\frac{1}{r^2}\frac{d}{dr}\left(r^2\frac{du}{dr}\right)=\begin{cases}-4\pi\rho & (r<R),\\ 0 & (r>R).\end{cases}$$

The arbitrary constants that appear in the general solution of this equation must be determined from the boundary conditions:

(1) The potential must remain finite as $r\to 0$ and it must vanish at infinity; (2) the potential of an electrostatic field must be a continuous function of the points in space, so that $\varphi_i(R)=\varphi_e(R)$; (3) $\left(\frac{\partial\varphi_i}{\partial r}\right)_{r=R}=\left(\frac{\partial\varphi_e}{\partial r}\right)_{r=R}$. This last condition means that the normal component of the vector **E** must not have a discontinuity on the surface of the sphere since the surface charge density is zero.

**130.** $e/r$.

**131.**

$$u=\begin{cases}u_0-\pi\rho r^2 & (r\leqslant a)\\ u_0-\pi\rho a^2\left(1+2\ln\frac{r}{a}\right) & (r\geqslant a)\end{cases};$$

$$\mathbf{E}=\begin{cases}2\pi\rho\mathbf{r} & (r<a),\\ 2\pi\rho\frac{a^2}{r^2}\mathbf{r} & (r>a),\end{cases}$$

where $u_0$ is the potential of the field on the axis of the cylinder. *Solution*: The problem leads to Poisson's integral equation $\Delta u=-4\pi\mu$, where $\mu=\rho$ for $r\leqslant a$ and $\mu=0$ for $r\geqslant a$. Because of the obvious symmetry of the field, this equation can be written in cylindrical coordinates, $r$, $\theta$, $z$ (with $z$-axis placed along the axis of the cylinder) in the form

$$\frac{1}{r}\frac{d}{dr}\left(r\frac{du}{dr}\right)=\begin{cases}-4\pi\rho & (r<a),\\ 0 & (r>a).\end{cases}$$

Solving this equation, we obtain

$$u=\begin{cases}u_i=-\pi\rho r^2+c_1\ln r+c_2 & (r\leqslant a),\\ u_e=c_3\ln r+c_4 & (r\geqslant a)\end{cases}$$

and the field intensity is

$$E=\begin{cases}E_i=-\frac{du_i}{dr}=2\pi\rho r-\frac{c_1}{r} & (r<a),\\ E_e=-\frac{du_e}{dr}=-\frac{c_3}{r} & (r>a).\end{cases}$$

To keep $E_i$ bounded for $r=0$, we must take $c_1=0$. Since $u_i \to c_2$ as $r \to 0$ (because we are taking $c_1=0$), we take $c_2=u_0$, which is the potential of the field on the axis of the cylinder. The constants $c_3$ and $c_4$ are determined by the requirement that the potential and the normal component of the vector E be continuous on the surface of the cylinder:

$$\varphi_i(a)=\varphi_e(a); \quad \left(\frac{d\varphi_i}{dr}\right)_{r=a}=\left(\frac{d\varphi_e}{dr}\right)_{r=a}.$$

**132.** The displacement $u(x,t)$ of the point $x$ from the equilibrium position at an arbitrary instant $t>0$ satisfies the equation

$$u_{tt}=a^2u_{xx} \qquad (-\infty<x<\infty, \quad t>0)$$

and the initial conditions

$$u(x,0)=\begin{cases} \frac{h}{c^2}(c^2-x^2) & (-c\leqslant x\leqslant c), \\ 0 & (-\infty<x\leqslant -c, \quad c\leqslant x<\infty). \end{cases}$$
$$u_t(x,0)=0.$$

**133.** The displacement $u(x,t)$ of the cross section with abscissa $x$ at an instant $t>0$ satisfies the equation

$$u_{xx}=\frac{1}{a^2}u_{tt} \qquad \left(a^2=\frac{E}{\rho}, \quad 0<x<l, \ t>0\right),$$

where $E$ is Young's modulus and $\rho$ is the line density. The additional conditions are:

$u(0,t)=0$ (the condition that the end $x=0$ be clamped)
$u_x(l,t)=0$ (the condition that the end $x=l$ be free)
$\left.\begin{aligned} u(x,0)&=\mu(x) \\ u_t(x,0)&=\nu(x) \end{aligned}\right\}$ the initial conditions $(0\leqslant x\leqslant l)$.

**134.**

$$134. \ \frac{\partial^2\theta}{\partial t^2}=a^2\frac{\partial^2\theta}{\partial x^2}, \quad a=\sqrt{\frac{GI}{k}},$$
$$\theta(0,t)=0, \quad \frac{\partial^2\theta(l,t)}{\partial t^2}=-c^2\frac{\partial\theta(l,t)}{\partial x}; \quad c^2=\frac{GI}{k_1};$$
$$\theta(x,0)=\varphi_0(x), \quad \frac{\partial\theta(x,0)}{\partial t}=\varphi_1(x) \qquad (0<x<l),$$

where $\theta$ is the angle of twist of the cross section of the rod with abscissa $x$, $G$ is the shear modulus, $I$ is the polar moment of inertia of the cross section, $k$ is the moment of inertia per unit length of the rod, and $k_1$ is the moment of inertia of the pulley about the axis of the rod. *Remark*: The term "torsional vibrations" of a rod is applied to vibrations such that the cross sections of the rod rotate with respect to each other while rotating about the axis of the rod.

**135.** (a) $u(x, t) = \sin x \cos t$; (b) $u(x, t) = A/a \sin x \sin at$.

**136.**

$$u(x, t) = \frac{1}{2}[\mu(x - at) + \mu(x + at)] + \\ + \frac{1}{2a}\int_{x-at}^{x+at} \nu(\xi)\, d\xi + \frac{a}{2T}\iint_{(D)} q(\xi, \tau)\, d\xi\, d\tau,$$

where $a^2 = T/\rho$ is the region of integration $(D)$ shown in Fig. 24, that is, a triangle whose sides are segments of the characteristics $x - at = \text{const.}$ and $x + at = \text{const.}$

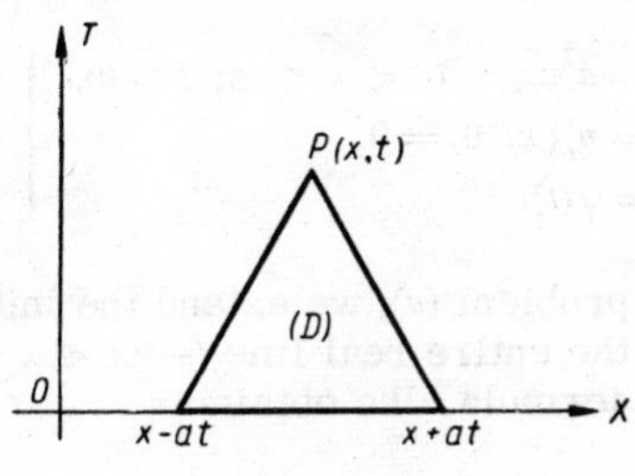


FIG. 24

**137.**

$$v(x, t) = e^{-\alpha t}\left\{\frac{1}{2}[\varphi(x - at) + \varphi(x + at)] + \\ + \frac{1}{2aC}[\psi(x - at) - \psi(x + at)]\right\},$$

$$I(x, t) = e^{-\alpha t}\left\{\frac{1}{2}[\psi(x - at) + \psi(x + at)] + \\ + \frac{1}{2aL}[\varphi(x - at) - \varphi(x + at)]\right\},$$

where

$$\alpha = \frac{R}{L}, \quad a = \frac{1}{\sqrt{LC}}.$$

*Hint*: The intensity $v = v(x, t)$ and the current $I(x, t)$ in a distortionless line satisfy the equations

$$v_{tt} = a^2 v_{xx}, \quad I_{tt} = a^2 I_{xx} \quad \left(a = \frac{1}{\sqrt{LC}}\right)$$

(See, for example, A. N. Tikhonov and A. A. Samarskiy, *Uravneniya matematicheskoy fiziki* (Equations of Mathematical Physics).) To integrate these equations, we set $v = e^{-\gamma t} w$, choosing $\gamma$ so that the coefficient $\partial w/\partial t$ will vanish.

**139.** *Hint*: Seek a solution for

$$u(x, t) = U(x, t) + v(x, t),$$

where $U(x, t)$ is the solution of the boundary-value problem

$$\left.\begin{aligned} &U''_{tt} = a^2 U''_{xx} \qquad (0 < x < \infty;\ t > 0) \\ &U(x, 0) = \mu(x), \quad U'_t(x, 0) = \nu(x) \\ &U(0, t) = 0, \end{aligned}\right\} \qquad (u)$$

and $v(x, t)$ is a solution of the problem

$$\left.\begin{aligned} &v''_{tt} = a^2 v''_{xx} \quad (0 < x < \infty;\ t > 0), \\ &v(x, 0) = v'_t(x, 0) = 0, \\ &v(0, t) = \psi(t). \end{aligned}\right\} \qquad (v)$$

To solve the problem $(u)$, we extend the initial conditions as odd functions to the entire real line $(-\infty < x < \infty)$ and we then use d'Alembert's formula. We obtain

$$U(x, t) = \begin{cases} \dfrac{\mu(x + at) - \mu(at - x)}{2} + \dfrac{1}{2a} \displaystyle\int_{at-x}^{x+at} \nu(\xi)\, d\xi & \text{for } t > \dfrac{x}{a}; \\[2ex] \dfrac{\mu(x + at) + \mu(x - at)}{2} + \dfrac{1}{2a} \displaystyle\int_{x-at}^{x+at} \nu(\xi)\, d\xi & \text{for } t < \dfrac{x}{a}. \end{cases}$$

The solution of problem $(v)$ is the function

$$v(x, t) = \begin{cases} \psi\left(t - \dfrac{x}{a}\right) & \text{for } t \geqslant \dfrac{x}{a}; \\[1ex] 0 & \text{for } t < \dfrac{x}{a}. \end{cases}$$

**140.** (a) $u(2\pi, 10) = \sin 2\pi^2$; (b) $u(2\pi, 10) = 0$.

**141.**

$$u(x, t) = \begin{cases} Ae^{-k\left(t-\frac{x}{a}\right)} & \text{for } t \geqslant \frac{x}{a}, \\ 0 & \text{for } 0 < t < \frac{x}{a}. \end{cases}$$

*Hint*: The problem consists in integrating the equation

$$u_{tt} = a^2 u_{xx} \quad (x > 0,\ t > 0)$$

with the conditions

$$u(0, t) = \mu(t) \quad (t > 0);$$
$$u(x, 0) = u_t(x, 0) = 0 \quad (0 < x < \infty).$$

Seek a solution in the form of a wave being propagated with velocity $a$ along the rod: $u(x, t) = \theta(x - at)$.

**142.** $u(x, t) = A \cos \omega (t - x/a)$ for $x \leqslant at$ and $u(x, t) = 0$ for $x > at$. The velocity of propagation of the wave $a = 80.8$ m/sec.

**143.**

$$u(x, t) = \begin{cases} \frac{aMv_0}{\gamma P_0 S}\left[1 - e^{\frac{\gamma P_0 S}{Ma^2}(x-at)}\right] & \text{for } x - at < 0, \\ 0 & \text{for } x - at > 0. \end{cases}$$

*Hint*: The problem consists in integrating the equation

$$u_{tt} = a^2 u_{xx},$$

where $u(x, t)$ is the condensation of the gas, that is, the relative change in the density of the vibrating gas $(\rho - \rho_0)/\rho$ (see V. I. Levin, *Metody matematicheskoy fiziki* [Methods of Mathematical Physics], p. 96) with the conditions

$$Mu_{tt}(0, t) = S\gamma P_0 u(0, t),$$
$$u(0, 0) = 0, \quad u_t(0, 0) = v_0, \quad u_t(x, 0) = 0 \quad (x > 0).$$

Here, $P_0$ is the initial pressure of the gas, $S$ is the area of a cross section of the tube, $\gamma = c_p/c_V$ is the ratio of the specific heat at constant pressure to the specific heat at constant volume, $a = \sqrt{\frac{c_p P_0}{c_V \rho_0}}$, and $\rho_0$ is the initial density of the gas.

**144.**

$$u(x, t) = \begin{cases} 0 & \text{for } t < \frac{x}{a}, \\ A \sin \omega \left(t - \frac{x}{a}\right) & \text{for } t > \frac{x}{a}. \end{cases}$$

**145.**

$$u(x, t) = \begin{cases} 0 & \text{for } t < \dfrac{x}{a}, \\ A \sin \dfrac{\omega}{a}(at - x) & \text{for } t > \dfrac{x}{a}. \end{cases}$$

**146.** At the instant $t_1 = l/2a$, all points of the string lie on the $X$-axis. At the instant $t_2 = l/a$, the string is in the position occupied by the mirror image of its original position with respect to the $X$-axis.

**147.** *Procedure*: The functions $\mu(x)$ and $\nu(x)$ should be extended as odd functions from the interval $[0, l]$ to the interval $[-l, 0]$ and then as periodic functions with period $2l$ to the entire $x$-axis. The function $\Phi(x, t)$, defined according to d'Alembert's formula in terms of the extensions described above of the original functions $\mu(x)$ and $\nu(x)$, gives an initial disturbance of an infinite string $(-\infty < x < \infty)$, that coincides with the desired disturbance on the interval $[0, l]$.

**148.**

$$S = \begin{cases} 0 & \text{for } 0 < t < \dfrac{r-R}{a}, \\ \dfrac{S_0(r - at)}{2r} & \text{for } \dfrac{r-R}{a} < t < \dfrac{r+R}{a}, \\ 0 & \text{for } \dfrac{r+R}{a} < t < \infty. \end{cases}$$

*Procedure*: The condensation $S(x, y, z, t)$ satisfies the wave equation

$$S_{tt} = a^2 \Delta S = a^2 \left( \frac{\partial^2 S}{\partial x^2} + \frac{\partial^2 S}{\partial y^2} + \frac{\partial^2 S}{\partial z^2} \right).$$

Between the condensation $S$ and the velocity potential $u$ of the gas, we have the relationship

$$S = \frac{1}{a^2} u'_t.$$

The problem amounts to integrating the wave equation above with the initial conditions

$$S \Big|_{t=0} = \begin{cases} S_0 & \text{for } r < R, \\ 0 & \text{for } r > R; \end{cases} \quad \frac{\partial S}{\partial t} \Big|_{t=0} = 0,$$

where $r$ is the distance from the coordinate origin (the center of the sphere is assumed to be at the origin) to a variable point $M(x, y, z)$. In solving the problem, one must remember that the initial vibrations of the gas are of a radial nature.

**149.**

$$u(x, t) = A \sin \frac{\pi x}{l} \cos \frac{\pi a t}{l} \quad (0 < x < l, \ t > 0).$$

**150.**

$$\omega_n = \frac{\pi a n}{l} = \frac{\pi n}{l} \sqrt{\frac{T}{\rho}} \quad (n = 1, 2, 3, \ldots).$$

**151.**

$$\omega_n = \frac{2n+1}{2l} \pi a \quad (n = 0, 1, 2, 3, \ldots),$$

where $a = \sqrt{\frac{E}{\rho}}$, $E$ is Young's modulus, and $\rho$ is the density of the rod. In the case in which a weight $M_0$ is attached to the free end, $\omega_n = \frac{a}{l} \gamma_n$ (for $n = 1, 2, \ldots$), where the $\gamma_n$ are the positive roots of the equation $\gamma \tan \gamma = M/M_0$, $M$ being the mass of the rod.

**152.** 632 vibrations per second.

**153.** The amplitudes are $H_n = \sqrt{A_n^2 + B_n^2}$; the period of vibration is

$$\tau_n = \frac{4l}{2n+1} \sqrt{\frac{\rho}{E}},$$

where

$$A_n = \frac{2}{l} \int_0^l \mu(\xi) \sin \lambda_n \xi \, d\xi,$$

$$B_n = \frac{2}{a \lambda_n l} \int_0^l \nu(\xi) \sin \lambda_n \xi \, d\xi,$$

$$\lambda_n = \frac{2n+1}{2l} \pi \quad (n = 0, 1, 2, 3, \ldots),$$

$\rho$ is the density of the rod, and $E$ is the modulus of elasticity of the material of which the rod is made.

*Procedure*: Remember that the stress is zero at the free end. Therefore, $u_x(l, t) = 0$. The harmonics

$$u_n(x, t) = (A_n \cos a\lambda_n t + B_n \sin a\lambda_n t) \sin \lambda_n x,$$

$$\lambda_n = \frac{2n+1}{2l} \pi \quad (n = 0, 1, 2, \ldots)$$

represent standing waves in the rod. If we write $u_n(x, t)$ in the formula

$$u_n(x, t) = H_n \sin(a\lambda_n t + \alpha_n)\sin\lambda_n x,$$
$$\left(\sin\alpha_n = \frac{A_n}{H_n}, \quad \cos\alpha_n = \frac{B_n}{H_n}\right),$$

we find

$$H_n = \sqrt{A_n^2 + B_n^2}.$$

The period is given by the formula

$$\tau_n = \frac{2\pi}{\omega_n} = \frac{2\pi}{a\lambda_n}, \quad a = \sqrt{\frac{E}{\rho}}.$$

The quantities $A_n$ and $B_n$ are determined in the course of solving the boundary-value problem.

**154.**

$$u(x, t) = \frac{32h}{\pi^3}\sum_{n=0}^{\infty}\frac{1}{(2n+1)^3}\sin\frac{(2n+1)\pi x}{l}\cos\frac{2n+1}{l}\pi a t,$$

where $h$ is the maximum initial deviation of the string from its equilibrium position. In the particular case mentioned,

$$u(x, t) = \cos at \sin x \qquad (0 < x < \pi, \ t > 0).$$

**155.**

$$u(x, t) =$$
$$= \sum_{n=0}^{\infty}\left[a_n\cos\frac{2n+1}{2l}\pi a t + b_n\sin\frac{2n+1}{2l}\pi a t\right]\sin\frac{2n+1}{2l}\pi x,$$

where

$$a_n = \frac{2}{l}\int_0^l \mu(x)\sin\frac{2n+1}{2l}\pi x\,dx,$$

$$b_n = \frac{4}{(2n+1)\pi a}\int_0^l \nu(x)\sin\frac{2n+1}{2l}\pi x\,dx.$$

*Procedure*: The problem amounts to integrating the equation

$$u_{tt} = a^2 u_{xx}, \quad a^2 = \frac{E}{\rho}$$

under the conditions

$$u(0, t)=0, \quad u_x(l, t)=0 \quad (t>0),$$
$$u(x, 0)=\mu(x), \quad u_t(x, 0)=\nu(x) \quad (0 \leqslant x \leqslant l),$$

where $u(x, t)$ is the displacement of the cross section whose abscissa is $x$, $\rho$ is the linear density, and $E$ is Young's modulus.

**156.**

$$E_n = \rho l h^2 \frac{a^2 l^2}{\pi^2 n^2 x_0 (l-x_0)^2} \sin \frac{\pi n x_0}{l}.$$

*Hint*: The energy of the $n$th harmonic (the $n$th standing wave $u_n$) of the transverse vibrations of the string is equal to

$$E_n = \frac{1}{2} \int_0^l \left[\rho \left(\frac{\partial u_n}{\partial t}\right)^2 + T\left(\frac{\partial u_n}{\partial x}\right)^2\right] dx,$$

where $T$ is the tension and $\rho$ is the linear density of the string.

**157.** The deviation $u(x, t)$ at an instant $t>0$ of the point on the string whose abscissa is $x$ is given by the formula

$$u(x, t) = \sum_{n=1}^{\infty} (a_n \cos \omega_n t + b_n \sin \omega_n t) \sin \frac{\pi n x}{l} + \frac{A}{\rho \omega^2}\left(\frac{\cos \frac{\omega}{a}\left(x-\frac{l}{2}\right)}{\cos \frac{\omega}{2a} l} - 1\right) \sin \omega t,$$

where

$$\omega_n = \frac{\pi n a}{l}, \quad a_n = \frac{2}{l} \int_0^l \mu(x) \sin \frac{\pi n x}{l} dx,$$
$$b_n = \frac{2}{\pi n a} \int_0^l \nu(x) \sin \frac{\pi n x}{l} dx.$$

*Hint*: First solve the problem of the purely forced vibrations of the string under the action of an external force equal to $A/\rho \sin \omega t$, where $\rho$ is the constant density of the string, and then seek a solution in the form

$$u_2(x, t) = X(x) \sin \omega t.$$

**159.**

$$u(x, t) = \frac{8\varepsilon l}{\pi^2} \sum_{n=0}^{\infty} \frac{(-1)^{n+1}}{(2n+1)^2} \sin \frac{2n+1}{2l} \pi x \cdot \cos \frac{2n+1}{2l} \pi a t,$$

where $a$ is the velocity of propagation of longitudinal waves in the rod.

*Hint*: The problem amounts to integrating the equation $u_{tt} = a^2 u_{xx}$ with the conditions

$$u_x(-l,\ t) = 0, \qquad u_x(l,\ t) = 0,$$
$$u(x,\ 0) = -\varepsilon x, \qquad u_t(x,\ 0) = 0.$$

**160.** For the flat hammer,

$$u(x,\ t) = \frac{4v_0 l}{\pi^2 a} \sum_{n=1}^{\infty} \frac{1}{n^2} \sin \frac{\pi n x_0}{l} \sin \frac{\pi n \delta}{l} \sin \frac{\pi n x}{l} \sin \frac{\pi n a t}{l},$$

for the sharp hammer,

$$u(x,\ t) = \frac{2P}{\pi a \rho} \sum_{n=1}^{\infty} \frac{1}{n} \sin \frac{\pi n x_0}{l} \sin \frac{\pi n x}{l} \sin \frac{\pi n a t}{l}.$$

**161.**

$$u(x,\ t) = -\frac{2lF_0}{\pi^2 T} \sum_{n=1}^{\infty} \frac{1}{n^2} \sin \frac{\pi n c}{l} \sin \frac{\pi n x}{l} \cos \frac{\pi n a t}{l}.$$

*Procedure*: The problem amounts to integrating the equation $u''_{tt} = a^2 u''_{xx}$ with the conditions

$$u(0,\ t) = u(l,\ t) = 0,$$
$$u(x,\ 0) = \mu(x), \quad u'_t(x,\ 0) = 0,$$

where the function $\mu(x)$ (the initial deviation) must first be found from the given condition. Obviously (see Fig. 25), to determine $\mu(x)$ it will be sufficient to find the maximum initial displacement $h$. It can be found from the condition of equilibrium. The projection onto the $U$-axis of the tensile force $T$ acting at a point $M$ of the string on the left portion $OM$ is $T_U = T \sin \alpha$. Analogously, the projection of the tensile force $T$ on the right portion $lM$ will be

$$T_U = T \sin \beta.$$

Obviously, the projection of the force $T$ onto the $X$-axis will be equal in magnitude on the two portions but opposite in sign. By applying d'Alembert's principle, we obtain

$$T(\sin \alpha + \sin \beta) = F_0.$$

Since the vibrations are of small amplitude, we may take

$$\sin \alpha \approx \tan \alpha = \frac{h}{c}.$$

Now, we easily obtain

$$h = \frac{F_0 c\,(l - c)}{lT}.$$

At this point, the determination of the initial shape of the string is obvious.

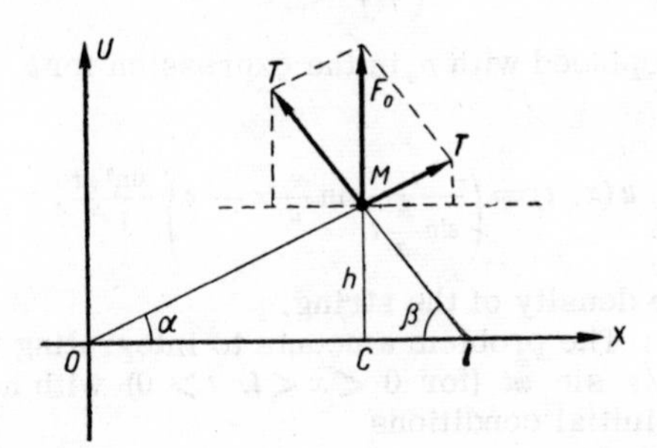


FIG. 25

**162.** The displacement of the section whose abscissa is $x$ at an instant $t > 0$ is

$$u(x,\ t) = \frac{8F_0 l}{E\pi^2 a} \sum_{n=0}^{\infty} (-1)^n \frac{\cos \frac{2n+1}{2l} \pi a t \sin \frac{2n+1}{2l} \pi x}{(2n+1)^2},$$

where $a^2 = E/\rho$, $E$ is Young's modulus, $\rho$ is the linear density, and $l$ is the length of the rod.

**163.**

$$u(x,\ t) = \sum_{n=1}^{\infty} T_n(t) \sin \frac{\pi n}{l} x,$$

where

$$T_n(t) = \begin{cases} e^{-kt}(a_n \cos q_n t + b_n \sin q_n t) & \text{for } \left(\frac{\pi n}{l}\right)^2 > k^2, \\ e^{-kt}(a_n \operatorname{ch} p_n t + b_n \operatorname{sh} p_n t) & \text{for } \left(\frac{\pi n}{l}\right)^2 < k^2, \end{cases}$$

$$q_n^2 = \left(\frac{\pi n}{l}\right)^2 - k^2, \quad p_n^2 = k^2 - \left(\frac{\pi n}{l}\right)^2;$$

$$a_n = \frac{2}{l} \int_0^l f(x) \sin \frac{\pi n x}{l}\, dx,$$

$$b_n = \frac{2}{l q_n} \int_0^l F(x) \sin \frac{\pi n x}{l}\, dx + \frac{k a_n}{q_n},$$

if

$$\left(\frac{\pi n}{l}\right)^2 > k^2.$$

If

$$\left(\frac{\pi n}{l}\right)^2 < k^2,$$

$q_n$ should be replaced with $p_n$ in the expression for $b_n$.

**164.**

$$u(x, t) = \left(\frac{l}{\sin\frac{\omega}{a} l} \sin\frac{\omega}{a} x - x\right) \frac{\sin^2 \omega t}{\rho\omega^2},$$

where $\rho$ is the density of the string.

*Procedure*: The problem amounts to integrating the equation $u_{tt} = a^2 u_{xx} + x/\rho \sin \omega t$ (for $0 < x < l$, $t > 0$) with homogeneous boundary and initial conditions

$$u(0, t) = u(l, t) = 0; \quad u(x, 0) = \frac{\partial u(x, 0)}{\partial t} = 0$$
$$(t > 0; \quad 0 < x < l).$$

We seek a solution in the form $u = X_1(x) \sin \omega t + X_2(x) \cos \omega t$. It should be borne in mind that it is always convenient to seek a solution of a problem dealing with purely forced vibrations of a string in this form if the external force is of the form $F = A \sin \omega t$, where $A$ is a function of $x$. In the present case, it is more convenient yet to seek a solution in the form $u = Xe^{i\omega t}$, where $X = X(x)$ is a function to be determined.

**165.**

$$u(x, t) = \frac{2}{l} \sum_{n=1}^{\infty} \left[\cos \omega_n t \int_0^l f(\xi) \sin\frac{\pi n}{l} \xi \, d\xi + \right.$$
$$\left. + \frac{l^2}{\pi^2 n^2 a^2} \sin \omega_n t \int_0^l g(\xi) \sin\frac{\pi n}{l} \xi \, d\xi\right] \sin\frac{\pi n}{l} x,$$

where $\omega_n = \frac{\pi^2 n^2 a^2}{l^2}$, $a^2 = \frac{EJ}{\rho S}$, $E$ is Young's modulus, $J$ is the moment of inertia of a cross section, $\rho$ is the density of the beam, and $S$ is the area of a cross section. *Hint*: The problem amounts to integration of the differential equation for transverse vibrations of a beam

$$u''_{tt} + a^2 u^{(\mathrm{IV})}_{x^4} = 0 \quad \left(a^2 = \frac{EJ}{\rho S}\right)$$

with the initial conditions

$$u(x, 0)=f(x) \quad u'_t(x, 0)=g(x)$$

and boundary conditions

$$u(0, t)=u''_{xx}(0, t)=u(l, t)=u''_{xx}(l, t)=0.$$

Use the method of separating the variables.

**166.**

$$v(x, t)=e^{-\frac{R}{2L}t}\sum_{n=0}^{\infty} a_n \sin\frac{2n+1}{2l}\pi x \sin(\omega_n t+\varphi_n),$$

where $\omega_n=\frac{(2n+1)\pi}{2l\sqrt{CL}}\sqrt{1-\frac{C^2R^2l^2}{\pi^2L(2n+1)^2}}$

(it is assumed that $L>\frac{C^2R^2l^2}{\pi^2}$),

$$a_n=\frac{4v_0}{\pi(2n+1)\sin\varphi_n}$$

and

$$\tan\varphi_n=2\omega_n\frac{L}{R}.$$

*Procedure*: The passage of an electric current through a conductor with the parameters $C$, $L$, $R$, and $G$ (the leakage) evenly distributed along the length of the conductor is characterized by a current $i$ and voltage $v$. These last are functions of the position of a point $x$ and the time $t$ and they satisfy the following system known as the telegraph equations:

$$\begin{aligned} i'_x+Cv'_t+Gv&=0,\\ v'_x+Li'_t+Ri&=0. \end{aligned} \tag{1}$$

From this system, we easily find equations for $i$ and $v$:

$$i''_{xx}=Ci''_{tt}+(CR+GL)i'_t+GRi, \tag{2}$$

$$v''_{xx}=CLv''_{tt}+(CR+GL)v'_t+GRv. \tag{3}$$

(See A. N. Tikhonov and A. A. Samarskiy, *Uravneniya matematicheskoy fiziki* (Equations of Mathematical Physics), 1951, p. 29.)

For problem 166, equation (3) takes the form

$$v''_{xx} = CLv''_{tt} + CRv'_t \quad (0 < x < l,\ t > 0), \tag{4}$$

since the assumption that the conductor is insulated implies that $G = 0$. The boundary and initial conditions take the form

$$v(0,\ t) = v'_x(l,\ t) = 0 \quad (t > 0), \tag{5}$$

$$v(x,\ 0) = v_0,\ v'_t(x,\ 0) = 0 \quad (0 < x < l). \tag{6}$$

If we set

$$u = e^{\lambda t} v \quad (v = e^{-\lambda t} \cdot u),$$

where $\lambda = R/2L$, equation (4) is reduced to the form

$$u''_{tt} = a^2 u''_{xx} + b^2 u, \tag{7}$$

where

$$a^2 = \frac{1}{CL}, \quad b^2 = \frac{R^2}{4L^2}.$$

For the function $u$, conditions (5) and (6) take the form

$$u(0,\ t) = u'_x(l,\ t) = 0, \tag{8}$$

$$u(x,\ 0) = v_0; \ -\lambda u(x,\ 0) + u'_t(x,\ 0) = 0. \tag{9}$$

If we set $u(x,\ t) = X(x)\,T(t)$ and separate the variables in equation (7), we obtain the following equation for $X(x)$

$$X'' + \lambda^2 X = 0 \quad (0 < x < l). \tag{10}$$

Because of conditions (8), the function $X(x)$ must satisfy the boundary conditions

$$X(0) = X(l) = 0. \tag{11}$$

The eigenvalues and eigenfunctions of problem (10) and (11) are

$$\lambda_n = \frac{\pi n}{l}, \quad X_n(x) = \sin \frac{\pi n}{l} x \quad (a = 1,\ 2,\ 3,\ \ldots)$$

(up to an arbitrary constant factor).

A solution of problem (7), (8), (9) should be sought in the form

$$u(x, t)=\sum_{n=1}^{\infty} T_n(t)\sin\frac{\pi n x}{l}. \tag{12}$$

The boundary conditions are satisfied. If we substitute (12) into (7), we obtain the differential equation for $T_n(t)$:

$$T_n''+\left[\left(\frac{\pi n a}{l}\right)^2-b^2\right]T=0. \tag{13}$$

By virtue of conditions (9), the function $T_n(t)$ must satisfy the conditions

$$T_n(0)=\frac{2}{l}\int_0^l v_0\sin\frac{\pi n x}{l}\,dx=\frac{2v_0}{\pi n}[(-1)^n-1], \tag{14}$$

$$T_n'(0)=\lambda_n T_n(0)=\frac{2v_0}{l}[(-1)^n-1]. \tag{15}$$

**168.** (a) $\omega_{mn}=\pi a\sqrt{\left(\frac{m}{l_1}\right)^2+\left(\frac{n}{l_2}\right)^2}$ (for $m$, $n=1, 2, 3, \ldots$), where $a=\sqrt{\frac{T}{\rho}}$, $T$ is the tension per unit length of the contour, and $\rho$ is the surface density of the membrane; (b) $\omega_{11}=\frac{\pi}{l}\sqrt{\frac{2T}{\rho}}$.

**169.** The eigenvalues are $\lambda_{mn}=\pi^2\left[\left(\frac{m}{a}\right)^2+\left(\frac{n}{b}\right)^2\right]$; the eigenfunctions (up to a constant factor) are

$$v_{mn}(x, y)=\sin\frac{\pi m x}{a}\sin\frac{\pi n y}{b} \qquad (m, n=1, 2, 3, \ldots).$$

**170.**

$$u(x, y, t)=\frac{64Al^4}{\pi^6}\sum_{m, n=0}^{\infty}\frac{\sin\frac{2n+1}{l}\pi x\cdot\sin\frac{2m+1}{l}\pi y}{(2n+1)^3(2m+1)^3}\times$$
$$\times\cos\sqrt{(2n+1)^2+(2m+1)^2}\,\frac{\pi a t}{l}.$$

**171.**

$$\varphi(x, y, t)=\frac{16A(l_1 l_2)^2}{\pi^6}\sum_{m, n=0}^{\infty}\frac{\sin\frac{2m+1}{l_1}\pi x\cdot\sin\frac{2n+1}{l_2}\pi y}{(2m+1)^3(2n+1)^3\omega_{mn}}\sin\omega_{mn}t,$$

where

$$\omega_{mn} = \pi a \sqrt{\left(\frac{2m+1}{l_1}\right)^2 + \left(\frac{2n+1}{l_2}\right)^2}.$$

**172.**

$$u(x, y, t) = \sum_{m, n=1}^{\infty} A_{mn}\left(\sin \omega t - \frac{\omega}{\omega_{mn}} \sin \omega_{mn} t\right) \times$$

$$\times \sin \frac{\pi m x}{l_1} \sin \frac{\pi n y}{l_2} \, (\omega \neq \omega_{mn}),$$

where

$$A_{mn} = \frac{4}{l_1 l_2 (\omega_{mn}^2 - \omega^2)} \int_0^{l_1} dx \int_0^{l_2} A^{(0)}(x, y) \sin \frac{\pi m x}{l_1} \times$$

$$\times \sin \frac{\pi n y}{l_2} \, dy \, (\omega_{mn} \neq \omega),$$

$$\omega_{mn} = \pi a \sqrt{\left(\frac{m}{l_1}\right)^2 + \left(\frac{n}{l_2}\right)^2}, \quad A^{(0)}(x, y) = \frac{1}{\rho} A(x, y).$$

If $\omega = \omega_{m_0 n_0}$ (this is the resonance frequency),

$$u(x, y, t) = \sum_{\substack{m, n=0 \\ (m \neq m_0, \, n \neq n_0)}}^{\infty} A_{mn}\left(\sin \omega t - \frac{\omega}{\omega_{mn}} \sin \omega_{mn} t\right) \sin \frac{\pi m x}{l_1} \times$$

$$\times \sin \frac{\pi n y}{l_2} + A_{m_0 n_0} (\sin \omega t - \omega t \cos \omega t) \sin \frac{m_0 \pi x}{l_1} \sin \frac{n_0 \pi y}{l_2},$$

where $A_{mn}$ is determined from the preceding formula and

$$A_{m_0 n_0} = \frac{2}{l_1 l_2 \omega} \int_0^{l_1} dx \int_0^{l_2} A^{(0)}(x, y) \sin \frac{\pi m_0 x}{l_1} \sin \frac{\pi n_0 y}{l_2} \, dy.$$

*Remark*: If the frequency $\omega_{m_0 n_0}$ is a multiple frequency, that is, if it corresponds to a multiple eigenvalue, we shall have not just one resonance term [the term not under the summation sign in the expression for $u(x, y, t)$] but a set of resonance terms of the form shown. The number of these terms is equal to the multiplicity of the frequency $\omega_{m_0 n_0}$.

*Hint*: The problem reduces to integrating the equation

$$u''_{tt} = a^2 (u''_{xx} + u''_{yy}) + A^{(0)}(x, y) \sin \omega t$$

$$\left(A^{(0)}(x, y) = \frac{1}{\rho} A(x, y)\right)$$

under the conditions

$$u|_{x=0}=u|_{x=l_1}=u|_{y=0}=u|_{y=l_2}=0,$$
$$u(x, y, 0)=0, \quad u'_t(x, y, 0)=0$$
$$(0<x<l_1, \ 0<y<l_2).$$

We neglect the reaction of the surrounding medium.

**173.**

$$u(x, y)=\frac{4v_0}{\pi}\sum_{m=0}^{\infty}\frac{\sin a_m x \sinh a_m y}{(2m+1)\sinh a_m b}+$$
$$+\frac{4v}{\pi}\sum_{m=0}^{\infty}\frac{\sin b_m y \sinh b_m(a-x)}{(2m+1)\sinh b_m a},$$

where

$$a_m=\frac{\pi(2m+1)}{a}, \quad b_m=\frac{\pi(2m+1)}{b}.$$

**174.**

$$\varphi(x, y)=B\frac{\sinh\frac{\pi(b-y)}{a}}{\sinh\frac{\pi b}{a}}\sin\frac{\pi x}{a}+$$
$$+\frac{8Ab^2}{\pi^3}\sum_{n=0}^{\infty}\frac{\sinh\frac{(2n+1)\pi(a-x)}{b}}{(2n+1)^3}\cdot\frac{\sin\frac{2n+1}{b}\pi y}{\sinh\frac{2n+1}{b}\pi a}.$$

**175.** The potential of the field is

$$u(x, y)=\frac{4v_0}{\pi}\sum_{m=0}^{\infty}e^{-\frac{2m+1}{b}\pi x}\cdot\frac{\sin\frac{2m+1}{b}\pi y}{2m+1}=$$
$$=\frac{2v_0}{\pi}\arctan\left(\frac{\sin\frac{\pi y}{b}}{\operatorname{sh}\frac{\pi x}{b}}\right).$$

Hint: The problem reduces to integrating Laplace's equation

$$u_{xx}+u_{yy}=0 \text{ in the region } G\begin{pmatrix}0<x<\infty,\\ 0<y<b.\end{pmatrix}$$

with the conditions

$$u|_{x=0}=v_0, \quad u|_{y=0}=u|_{y=b}=0$$
$$u(x, y)<\infty \quad \text{as} \quad x\to\infty.$$

To obtain a solution in closed form, one should use the expansion

$$\sum_{m=0}^{\infty}\frac{e^{-(2m+1)x}}{2m+1}\sin(2m+1)y=\frac{1}{2}\arctan\frac{\sin y}{\sinh x} \quad (x>0).$$

**176.**

$$u(x, y)=u_1(x, y)+u_2(x, y),$$

where

$$u_1(x, y)=\sum_{n=1}^{\infty}\left[\frac{\alpha_n^{(1)}+\alpha_n^{(2)}}{2\cosh\frac{\pi nb}{2a}}\cosh\frac{\pi ny}{a}+\frac{\alpha_n^{(1)}-\alpha_n^{(2)}}{2\sinh\frac{\pi nb}{2a}}\sinh\frac{\pi ny}{a}\right]\times$$
$$\times\sin\frac{\pi nx}{a},$$

$$u_2(x, y)=\sum_{n=1}^{\infty}\left[\frac{\delta_n^{(1)}+\delta_n^{(2)}}{2\cosh\frac{\pi na}{2b}}\cosh\frac{\pi n}{b}\left(x-\frac{a}{2}\right)+\frac{\delta_n^{(1)}-\delta_n^{(2)}}{2\sinh\frac{\pi na}{2b}}\times\right.$$
$$\left.\times\sinh\frac{\pi n}{b}\left(x-\frac{a}{2}\right)\right]\sin\frac{\pi n}{b}\left(y+\frac{b}{2}\right),$$

$$\alpha_n^{(1)}=\frac{2}{a}\int_0^a\varphi_1(\xi)\sin\frac{\pi n}{a}\xi\,d\xi; \quad \alpha_n^{(2)}=\frac{2}{a}\int_0^a\varphi_2(\xi)\sin\frac{\pi n}{a}\xi\,d\xi;$$

$$\delta_n^{(1)}=\frac{2}{b}\int_{-\frac{b}{2}}^{\frac{b}{2}}\psi_1(\eta)\sin\frac{\pi n}{b}\left(\eta+\frac{b}{2}\right)d\eta;$$

$$\delta_n^{(2)}=\frac{2}{b}\int_{-\frac{b}{2}}^{\frac{b}{2}}\psi_2(\eta)\sin\frac{\pi n}{b}\left(\eta+\frac{b}{2}\right)d\eta.$$

*Procedure*: The solution of the problem may be obtained as the sum of the solutions of the following two simpler problems:

$$\Delta u_i\equiv\frac{\partial^2 u_i}{\partial x^2}+\frac{\partial^2 u_i}{\partial y^2}=0 \qquad (i=1, 2),$$

$$u_1=\begin{cases}\varphi_1(x) & \text{for } y=\frac{b}{2}\\ \varphi_2(x) & \text{for } y=-\frac{b}{2}\\ 0 & \text{for } x=0 \text{ and } x=a\end{cases} \qquad u_2=\begin{cases}\psi_1(y) & \text{for } x=0,\\ \psi_2(y) & \text{for } x=a\\ 0 & \text{for } y=\pm\frac{b}{2}.\end{cases}$$

By means of the coordinate transformation

$$x' = y + \frac{b}{2}; \quad y' = x - \frac{a}{2}$$

the problem $(u_2)$ reduces to the probelm $(u_1)$. However, the roles of the numbers $a$ and $b$ are reversed and, instead of the functions $\varphi_1$ and $\varphi_2$, we shall have $\psi_1$ and $\psi_2$.

**177.** $u(x, y) = y(\cos x - 1/2)$.

**178.** The solution of Poisson's equation in the region $D$ that vanishes on the boundary of $D$ is

$$u(x, y) = x(a - x) - \frac{8a^2}{\pi^3} \sum_{n=1, 3, 5, \dots} \frac{\cosh \frac{\pi n y}{2a}}{n^3 \cosh \frac{\pi n b}{a}} \sin \frac{\pi n x}{a}$$

$$M = 2G\vartheta \left\{ \frac{a^3 b}{6} - \frac{32a^4}{\pi^5} \sum_{n=1, 3, 5, \dots} \frac{1}{n^5} \tanh \frac{\pi n b}{2a} \right\}.$$

The tangential stresses can be found by differentiating the equation for $u(x, y)$.

**179*.**

$$u(x, y) = \frac{4pa}{\pi^2 T} \sum_{n=0}^{\infty} \left( 1 - \frac{\cosh \frac{2n+1}{2a} \pi y}{\cosh \frac{2n+1}{2a} \pi b} \right) \cdot \frac{\cos \frac{2n+1}{2a} \pi x}{(2n+1)^2}$$

Another form of the solution is

$$u(x, y) = \frac{4pb}{\pi^2 T} \sum_{n=0}^{\infty} \frac{(-1)^n}{(2n+1)^2} \cdot \frac{\sinh \frac{2n+1}{2a} \pi (a - |x|)}{\cosh \frac{2n+1}{2b} \pi a} \times$$
$$\times \cos \frac{2n+1}{2b} \pi y$$

*Procedure*: First, assume that the external line load $p$ is uniformly distributed along some strip $(|x| < \varepsilon, |y| < b)$. Then, the problem reduces to integrating Poisson's equation:

$$\frac{\partial^2 u}{\partial x^2} + \frac{\partial^2 u}{\partial y^2} = -\frac{q(x, y)}{T} = \begin{cases} -\frac{p}{2\varepsilon T} & (|x| < \varepsilon), \\ 0 & (|x| > \varepsilon). \end{cases}$$

with the homogeneous boundary conditions

$$u|_{x=\pm a} = u|_{y=\pm b} = 0$$

Now take the limit as $\varepsilon \to 0$. Here, $q$ is the external load per unit of area, and $T$ is the tension per unit length of contour of the membrane.

**180***. The problem amounts to integrating the equation

$$\frac{\partial^2 u}{\partial t^2} = a^2\left(\frac{\partial^2 u}{\partial x^2} + \frac{\partial^2 u}{\partial y^2}\right) + \frac{1}{\rho}\frac{\partial P_0}{\partial t}$$

with the conditions

$$\left.\frac{\partial u}{\partial x}\right|_{x=0} = \left.\frac{\partial u}{\partial x}\right|_{x=a} = \left.\frac{\partial u}{\partial y}\right|_{y=0} = \left.\frac{\partial u}{\partial y}\right|_{y=b} = 0$$

$$u(x, y, 0) = 0, \quad u_t(x, y, 0) = 0$$

where $a^2 = gh$, $g$ being the acceleration due to gravity.

**181.** (a) $u(x, t) = \frac{8c}{\pi^3} \sum_{n=0}^{\infty} \frac{e^{-\frac{(2n+1)^2 \pi^2 a^2}{l^2} t}}{(2n+1)^3} \sin \frac{(2n+1)\pi x}{l}$;

(b) $u(x, t) = u_0 + \sum_{n=0}^{\infty} a_n e^{-a^2 \lambda_n^2 t} \cdot \cos \lambda_n x$,

where

$$a_n = \frac{2}{l}\int_0^l \varphi(x) \cos \lambda_n x \, dx + \frac{(-1)^{n+1} \cdot 4u_0}{(2n+1)\pi}, \quad \lambda_n = \frac{2n+1}{2l}\pi$$

в) $$v(x, t) = -\frac{2A\omega}{\pi} \sum_{n=1}^{\infty} \frac{1}{n} e^{-\left(\frac{\pi n a}{l}\right)^2 t} \times$$

$$\times \sin \frac{\pi n x}{l} \int_0^t e^{\lambda_n^2 \xi} \cos \omega\xi \, d\xi$$

where $\lambda_n = \pi n a / l$.

**182.** $T(x, t) = 50° e^{-0{,}004t} \sin \frac{2\pi x}{l}$.

**183.**

$$T(x, t) = \frac{1}{l}\int_0^l T(x, 0)\, dx +$$

$$+ \frac{2}{l}\sum_{n=1}^{\infty} e^{-\frac{\pi^2 n^2 t}{l^2}} \cos \frac{\pi n x}{l} \int_0^l T(x, 0) \cos \frac{\pi n x}{l} dx$$

The reader can continue the calculations.

**184.** *Procedure*: The heat-flow equation in a ring is of the form

$$u_t = a^2 u_{xx} - qu \tag{1}$$

where $a$ and $q$ are positive constants, $t$ denotes the time, $x$ is the length of wire as measured along its axis from some chosen zero point, $u = u(x, t)$ is the temperature of the cross section whose abscissa is $x$ at the instant $t$. If we set $u = ve^{-at}$, Eq. (1) is reduced to the form

$$v'_t = a^2 v''_{xx},$$

and the problem is reduced to integrating this equation with the conditions

$$v(x, 0) = f(x), \quad v(x + 2\pi, t) = v(x, t)$$

(The last condition indicates the periodicity (with period $2\pi$) of the desired function and fills the role of a boundary condition.)

**185.** $u(r, t) = \sum_{n=1}^{\infty} A_n e^{-a^2\lambda_n^2 t} \cdot \sin \frac{\lambda_n r}{r}$,

where

$$A_n = \frac{2}{R} \frac{R^2\lambda_n^2 + (Rh - 1)^2}{R^2\lambda_n^2 + (Rh - 1)Rh} \int_0^R r f(r) \sin \lambda_n r \, dr,$$

and the $\lambda_n$ are the positive roots of the equation

$$\tan \lambda_n R = \frac{\lambda_n R}{1 - Rh}.$$

*Procedure*: Because of the radial symmetry of the problem, the heat-flow equation becomes

$$\frac{\partial u}{\partial t} = a^2 \left( \frac{\partial^2 u}{\partial r^2} + \frac{2}{r} \frac{\partial u}{\partial r} \right)$$

If we make the substitution $u = v/r$, this equation becomes the following one:

$$\frac{\partial v}{\partial t} = a^2 \frac{\partial^2 v}{\partial r^2} \quad \begin{pmatrix} 0 < r < R, \\ 0 < t < \infty \end{pmatrix}$$

The boundary condition is transformed into the condition

$$\frac{\partial v}{\partial r} = \frac{1-hR}{R} v \quad (r=R,\ t>0)$$

and the new initial condition is

$$v(r,\ 0) = rf(r) \quad (0<r<R).$$

To solve the problem, use Fourier's method.

**187.**

$$u(r,\ t) = \sum_{n=1}^{\infty} \frac{\sin \mu_n \frac{r}{R}}{r} \cdot \frac{2}{R} \int_0^R rf(r) \sin \mu_n \frac{r}{R}\, dr \cdot e^{-\mu_n^2 \frac{at}{R^2}}$$

where $\mu_n = n\pi$ (for $n = 1, 2, 3, \ldots$). For $f(r) = t_0 =$ const., we obtain

$$u(r,\ t) = t_0 \sum_{n=1}^{\infty} (-1)^{n+1} \frac{2}{\mu_n} \frac{R \sin \mu_n \frac{r}{R}}{r} e^{-\mu_n^2 \frac{at}{R^2}}.$$

*Procedure*: The problem amounts to integrating the equation

$$\frac{\partial u(r,\ t)}{\partial t} = a^2 \left( \frac{\partial^2 u(r,\ t)}{\partial r^2} + \frac{2}{r} \frac{\partial u(r,\ t)}{\partial r} \right) \quad (0<r<R,\ t>0)$$

with the conditions

$$u(r,\ 0) = f(r),$$
$$u(R,\ t) = t_c = 0^\circ$$
$$u(0,\ t) < \infty,$$
$$\frac{\partial u(0,\ x)}{\partial x} = 0.$$

The last condition is the condition of symmetry. The differential equation can be written in the form

$$\frac{\partial [ru(r,\ t)]}{\partial t} = a^2 \frac{\partial^2 [ru(r,\ t)]}{\partial r^2}.$$

Use the method of separating the variables.

**188.**

$$u(x,\ t) = \frac{4T_0}{\pi} \sum_{n=1}^{\infty} \frac{(-1)^{n-1}}{2n-1} e^{-\frac{(2n-1)^2 \pi^2 a^2}{4l^2}} \cdot \cos \frac{2n-1}{2l} \pi x$$

*Hint*: The problem amounts to integrating the equation $u'_t = a^2 u''_{xx}$ with the initial condition $u(x, 0) = T_0$ and the boundary conditions

$$u'_x(0, t) = 0; \quad u(l, t) = 0$$

(The temperature of the external medium is assumed to be 0°.)

**189.** *Hint*: To use the method of separating the variables, it is necessary to have homogeneous boundary conditions. By means of the substitution

$$v(x, t) = u(x, t) - u_l(t),$$

the boundary conditions of the problem are replaced with the homogeneous conditions

$$v'_x\Big|_{x=0} = 0; \quad hv\Big|_{x=l} = -kv'_x\Big|_{x=l}$$

**190.** $u'_t - a^2 u''_{xx} - b^2 (U - u) = g$, where $a^2 = k/c\rho$ and $b$ is the thermal conductivity of the surrounding medium, $U$ is the temperature of the medium, and $g$ is the heat source density in the rod.

**191.** $u(x, y) = \sum_{n=0}^{\infty} C_n \sinh \frac{2n+1}{a} \pi y \sin \frac{2n+1}{a} \pi x$, where

$$C_n = \frac{4T}{(2n+1)\pi \sinh(2n+1)\pi}.$$

**192.**

$$u\left(0, \frac{1}{2}b\right) = 2T \sum_{n=1}^{\infty} \frac{\sin \gamma_n}{\gamma_n + \sin \gamma_n \cos \gamma_n} \cdot \frac{\sinh \gamma_n \frac{b}{2a}}{\sinh \gamma_n \frac{b}{a}},$$

where the $\gamma_n$ are the positive roots of the equation $\tan \gamma = ah/\gamma$ numbered in increasing order for $n = 1, 2, 3, \ldots$, the constant $h$ being the coefficient of heat exchange.

**193.**

$$u(x, t) = \frac{2Ql}{c\rho\pi^2 a^2} \sum_{n=1}^{\infty} \frac{1}{n^2}\left(1 - e^{-\frac{\pi^2 n^2 a^2}{l^2} t}\right) \sin \frac{\pi n x_0}{l} \sin \frac{\pi n x}{l}$$

The problem reduces to the boundary-value problem

$$u_t = a^2 u_{xx} + \frac{Q}{c\rho} \delta(x - x_0) \quad (0 < x < l, \ t > 0)$$

$$u(0, t) = u(l, t) = 0 \quad (t > 0),$$

$$u(x, 0) = 0 \quad (0 < x < l),$$

where $\delta(\xi)$ is the delta function.

**194.** $f(x)=\frac{2}{\pi}\int_0^\infty \frac{\sin u}{u}\cos ux\,du.$

**195.** $f(x)=e^{-kx};\ \varphi(x)=e^{-kx}.$

**197.** (a) $u(x,t)=xt^3/6;$

(b) $u(x,t)=\frac{1}{2a\sqrt{\pi t}}\int_{-\infty}^{\infty}\mu(\xi)e^{-\frac{(x-\xi)^2}{4a^2t}}d\xi$; for $\mu=T_0$ we set: $u(x,t)=T_0;$

(c) $u(x,t)=\int_{-\infty}^{\infty}\left\{M(\omega)e^{-a^2\omega^2t}+\int_0^t G(\omega,\tau)e^{-a^2\omega^2(t-\tau)}d\tau\right\}\cdot e^{i\omega x}\,d\omega$

where

$$M(\omega)=\frac{1}{2\pi}\int_{-\infty}^{\infty}\mu(x)e^{-i\omega x}dx,$$

$$G(\omega,t)=\frac{1}{2\pi}\int_{-\infty}^{\infty}f(x,t)e^{i\omega x}dx.$$

**198.**

(a) $u(x,t)=\begin{cases}0 & \text{for}\quad 0<t<\frac{x}{a}\\ \left(t-\frac{x}{a}\right)^2 & \text{for}\quad t>\frac{x}{a}\end{cases}$

*Hint*: Use the Fourier sine transformation.

(b) $u(x,t)=\frac{1}{2a\sqrt{\pi t}}\int_0^\infty\left(e^{-\frac{(x-\xi)^2}{4a^2t}}-e^{-\frac{(x+\xi)^2}{4a^2t}}\right)f(\xi)\,d\xi.$

*Hint*: Use the Fourier sine transformation, noting that

$$\int_0^\infty e^{-\alpha^2x^2}\cos\beta x\,dx=\frac{\sqrt{\pi}}{2\alpha}e^{-\frac{\beta^2}{4\alpha^2}}.$$

(c) $u(x,t)=\frac{1}{2a\sqrt{\pi t}}\int_0^\infty\left(e^{-\frac{(x-\xi)^2}{4a^2t}}+e^{-\frac{(x+\xi)^2}{4a^2t}}\right)f(\xi)\,d\xi.$

**199.**

$$u(x,t)=-\frac{2}{\pi}\int_0^\infty\left(\int_0^\infty f(y)\sin\lambda y\,dy\right)e^{-\lambda x}\sin\lambda y\,d\lambda.$$

**200.** $u(x,t)=U_\infty(1-e^{-b^2t})+$

$$+\frac{e^{-b^2t}}{2a\sqrt{\pi t}}\int_{-\infty}^{\infty}f(\xi)e^{-\frac{(x-\xi)^2}{4a^2t}}d\xi+\frac{e^{-b^2t}}{2a\sqrt{\pi t}}\int_0^\infty\frac{d\tau}{\sqrt{t-\tau}}\int_{-\infty}^{\infty}[g(\xi,\tau)+$$

$$+b^2(U-U_\infty)]e^{b^2\tau-\frac{(x-\xi)^2}{4a^2(t-\tau)}}d\xi;$$

For $U = U_\infty =$ const., we have

$$u(x, t) = U_\infty(1 - e^{-b^2t}) + \frac{e^{-b^2t}}{2a\sqrt{\pi t}} \int_{-\infty}^{\infty} f(\xi) e^{-\frac{(x-\xi)^2}{4a^2t}} d\xi.$$

*Procedure*: By means of the substitution $u = U_\infty + ve^{-b^2t}$, where $U_\infty$ is the temperature of the outside space at infinity, the equation of the problem can be reduced to the following equation for the new function $v(x, t)$:

$$v_t - a^2 v_{xx} = [g + b^2(U - U_\infty)] e^{b^2t}$$

(the reader should verify this) with initial conditions

$$v(x, 0) = u(x, 0) - U_\infty = f(x) - U_\infty.$$

**203.**

$$J_{\frac{1}{2}}(x) = \sqrt{\frac{2}{\pi x}} \sin x; \quad J_{-\frac{1}{2}}(x) = \sqrt{\frac{2}{\pi x}} \cos x;$$

$$J_{\frac{3}{2}}(x) = \sqrt{\frac{2}{\pi x^3}} \sin x - \sqrt{\frac{2}{\pi x}} \cos x.$$

*Procedure*: We have

$$J_{\frac{1}{2}}(x) = \frac{\sqrt{x}}{\sqrt{2}\,\Gamma\left(\frac{3}{2}\right)} \left(1 - \frac{x^2}{2\cdot 3} + \right.$$

$$\left. + \frac{x^4}{2\cdot 4\cdot 3\cdot 5} - \frac{x^6}{2\cdot 4\cdot 6\cdot 3\cdot 5\cdot 7} + \ldots \right) =$$

$$= \frac{1}{\sqrt{2x}\,\Gamma\left(\frac{3}{2}\right)} \left(x - \frac{x^3}{3!} + \frac{x^5}{5!} - \frac{x^7}{7!} + \ldots \right) =$$

$$= \frac{1}{\sqrt{2x}\,\Gamma\left(\frac{3}{2}\right)} \sin x.$$

But

$$\Gamma\left(\frac{3}{2}\right) = \frac{1}{2}\Gamma\left(\frac{1}{2}\right) = \frac{1}{2}\int_0^\infty e^{-x}\frac{dx}{\sqrt{x}} = \int_0^\infty e^{-t^2} dt = \frac{\sqrt{\pi}}{2}.$$

We proceed analogously in the evaluation of $J_{-\frac{1}{2}}(x)$. To evaluate $J_{\frac{3}{2}}(x)$, we make the substitution $p = 1/2$ in the last formula of problem 202.

**204.** (a) $y = C_1 J_n(\alpha x) + C_2 N_n(\alpha x)$;
(b) *Hint*: Use the substitution $z = \sqrt{x}\, y$;
(c) $y = 1/x^2\,(C_1 J_2(x) + C_2 N_2(x))$, where $N_k$ is Bessel's function of the second kind of order k.

*Procedure*: Bessel's equation $x^2y'' + xy' + (x^2 - p^2)y = 0$, where $p \geqslant 0$, can, by the substitution $y = x^p z$, be reduced to the equation

$$z'' + \frac{2p+1}{x} z' + z = 0.$$

Setting $p = 2$ gives equation (c) of the problem.

**206.** (a) $x^p = \sum_{n=1}^{\infty} C_n J_p(\lambda_n x)$, where

$$C_n = \frac{2}{\lambda_n J_{p+1}(\lambda_n)} \left(p \geqslant -\frac{1}{2},\ 0 < x < 1\right);$$

(b) $$x^3 = 16 \sum_{n=1}^{\infty} \frac{J_3\left(\frac{1}{2}\lambda_n x\right)}{\lambda_n J_4(\lambda_n)} \qquad (0 \leqslant x < 2).$$

**207.**

$$P_0(x) = 1;\ P_1(x) = \cos\theta = x;$$
$$P_2(x) = \frac{1}{2}(3\cos^2\theta - 1) = \frac{1}{2}(3x^2 - 1);$$
$$P_3(x) = \frac{1}{2}(5\cos^3\theta - 3\cos\theta) = \frac{1}{2}(5x^3 - 3x^2);$$
$$P_4(x) = \frac{1}{8}(35x^4 - 30x^3 + 3).$$

**208.**

$$P_n(1) = 1,\ P_n(-1) = (-1)^n,$$
$$P_n(0) = \begin{cases} (-1)^{\frac{n}{2}} \cdot \dfrac{1\cdot 3\cdot 5 \ldots (n-1)}{2\cdot 4\cdot 6 \ldots n} & \text{for } n \text{ even}, \\ 0 & \text{for } n \text{ odd}. \end{cases}$$

**209.**

$$\varphi(r,\ \theta) = \sum_{n=0}^{\infty} \left(\frac{1}{r}\right)^n P_n(\cos\theta) \qquad (r > 1);$$
$$f(x) = \frac{1}{2} + \frac{3}{2^2} P_1(x) - \frac{7\cdot 2!}{2^4\cdot 2!\,1!} P_2(x) + \frac{11\cdot 4!}{2^6\cdot 3!\,2!} P_3(x) - \ldots$$

**211.**

$$u(r, \theta)=\begin{cases}\sum_{n=0}^{\infty} A_n\left(\frac{r}{R}\right)^n P_n(\cos\theta) & (r<R),\\ \sum_{n=0}^{\infty} A_n\left(\frac{R}{r}\right)^{n+1} P_n(\cos\theta) & (r>R),\end{cases}$$

where

$$A_n=\frac{2n+1}{2}\int_0^{\pi} f(\theta) P_n(\cos\theta)\sin\theta\, d\theta.$$

In the particular case, $u(r, \theta)=1/3\,(1-r^2)+r^2\cos^2\theta$.

**212.**

$$u(r, t)=\frac{2Pa}{\pi\varepsilon T}\sum_{n=1}^{\infty}\frac{J_1\left(\gamma_n\frac{\varepsilon}{R}\right)}{\gamma_n^2 J_1^2(\gamma_n)}\cdot J_0\left(\gamma_n\frac{r}{R}\right)\sin\frac{\gamma_n at}{R},$$

where the $\gamma_n$ are the successive positive roots of the equation $J_0(\gamma)=0$, $a=\sqrt{\frac{T}{\rho}}$, $T$ is the tension per unit length of contour, and $\rho$ is the surface density of the membrane.

*Procedure*: The problem amounts to integrating the equation

$$\frac{\partial^2 u}{\partial r^2}+\frac{1}{r}\frac{\partial u}{\partial r}-\frac{1}{a^2}\frac{\partial^2 u}{\partial t^2}=0$$

with the conditions

$u(0, t)$ is bounded;
$u(R, t)=0$;

$$u(r, 0)=0;\quad \frac{\partial u(r, 0)}{\partial t}=\begin{cases}\frac{P}{\pi\varepsilon^2\rho} & \text{for } 0\leqslant r<\varepsilon,\\ 0 & \text{for } \varepsilon<r\leqslant R,\end{cases}$$

where $\rho$ is the surface density of the membrane, assumed to be constant.

**213.**

$$u(r, t)=-\frac{q}{\rho\omega^2}\left[1-\frac{J_0\left(\frac{\omega r}{a}\right)}{J_0\left(\frac{\omega R}{a}\right)}\right]\sin(\omega t+\psi),$$

where $a=\sqrt{\frac{T}{\rho}}$, $T$ is the tension per unit length of contour, $\rho$ is the surface density of the membrane, and $J_0(x)$ is Bessel's function of the first kind of order zero.

**214.**

$$u(r, t)=\frac{2a}{T}\sum_{n=1}^{\infty}\frac{r_2 J_1\left(\frac{\gamma_n r_2}{R}\right)-r_1 J_1\left(\frac{\gamma_n r_1}{R}\right)}{\gamma_n^2 J_1^2(\gamma_n)}\times$$
$$\times J_0\left(\gamma_n\frac{r}{R}\right)\cdot\int_0^t q(\tau)\sin\frac{\gamma_n a(t-\tau)}{R}\,d\tau,$$

where $a=\sqrt{\frac{T}{\rho}}$ and the $\gamma_n$ are the positive roots of the equation $J_0(\gamma)=0$.

**215.**

$$u(0, t)=b\sum_{k=1}^{\infty}B_k\cos\omega_k t$$

where $B_k=b\left(\frac{2}{\mu_k}\right)^3\frac{1}{J_1(\mu_k)}$, $\mu_k$ is the $k$th positive root of the equation $J_0(\mu)=0$, and $\omega_k=a\frac{\mu_k}{R}$ is the angular frequency of the $k$th harmonic of the membrane.

The period of the fundamental tone is $T_1=\frac{2\pi}{\mu_1}R\sqrt{\frac{\gamma}{T}}\approx 0.00596$ sec, $\gamma$ being the surface density of the membrane.

**216.** *Solution*: We place the origin of a spherical coordinate system at the center of the sphere and we direct the $Z$-axis opposite to the direction of flow of the liquid (see Fig. 26). The velocity potential $u$ satisfies the equation

$$\frac{\partial}{\partial r}\left(r^2\frac{\partial u}{\partial r}\right)+\frac{1}{\sin\theta}\frac{\partial}{\partial\theta}\left(\sin\theta\frac{\partial u}{\partial\theta}\right)=0. \qquad (1)$$

We see from the drawing that the normal component of the velocity of a particle of the liquid on the surface of the sphere is

$$AB=a\cos(\pi-\theta).$$

From this we obtain the boundary condition

$$\left.\frac{\partial u}{\partial r}\right|_{r=R}=-a\cos\theta. \qquad (2)$$

We seek a solution of the problem (1), (2) in the form of a series of Legendre polynomials:

$$u(r, \theta) = \sum_{n=0}^{\infty} C_n P_n(\cos\theta)\left(\frac{R}{r}\right)^{n+1} \qquad (r > R).$$

On the basis of condition (2), we have

$$-\frac{1}{R}\sum_{n=0}^{\infty}(n+1)C_n P_n(\cos\theta) = -a\cos\theta.$$

This equation will hold if

$$C_0 = 0; \quad C_1 = -\frac{Ra}{2}, \quad C_2 = C_3 = \ldots = 0.$$

Consequently, the desired solution is

$$u(r, \theta) = \frac{aR^3}{2r^2}\cos\theta.$$

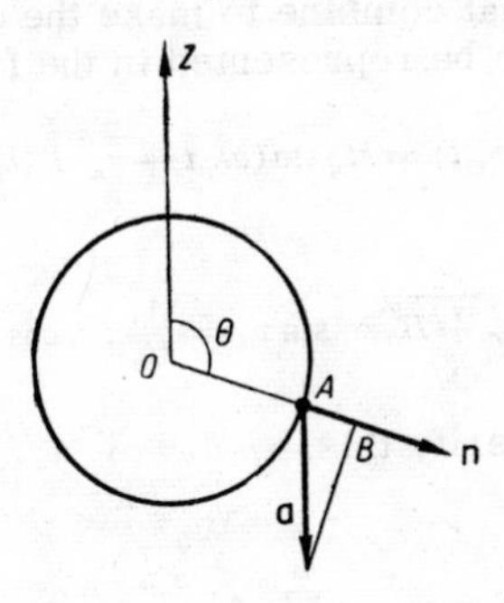


FIG. 26

**217.** The displacement of a point on the membrane is given by the series

$$u(r, t) = \sum_{n=1}^{\infty}(A_n\cos a\lambda_n t + B_n\sin a\lambda_n t)\, J_0(\lambda_n r),$$

where

$$A_n = \frac{2}{R^2 J_1^2(\mu_n)}\int_0^R r f(r) J_0(\lambda_n r)\, dr,$$

$$B_n = \frac{2}{\lambda_n R^2 J_1^2(\mu_n)\, a} \int_0^R r g(r) J_0(\lambda_n r)\, dr,$$

Here, $f(r)$ and $g(r)$ are respectively the initial displacement and the initial velocity of a point on the membrane:

$$u(r, 0) = f(r), \quad \frac{\partial u(r, 0)}{\partial t} = g(r)$$

and $\mu_n$ is the $n$th positive zero of the function $J_0(\mu)$, $\lambda_n = \mu_n/R$, and

$$a = \sqrt{\frac{T}{\rho}}.$$

**218.** The natural frequencies are $\omega_n = a\lambda_n = \frac{a\mu_n}{R} = \frac{\mu_n}{R}\sqrt{\frac{T}{\rho}}$. The amplitude of the vibrations of each tone is equal to $H_n |J_0(\lambda_n r)|$, where $H_n = \sqrt{A_n^2 + B_n^2}$, $A_n$ and $B_n$ having the values indicated in the answer to problem 217.

*Hint*: The individual harmonic vibrations $(A_n \cos a\lambda_n t + B_n \sin a\lambda_n t)\, J_0(\lambda_n r)$, that combine to make the composite vibration of the membrane can be represented in the form

$$u_n(r, t) = H_n \sin(a\lambda_n t + \alpha_n)\, J_0(\lambda_n r),$$

where

$$H_n = \sqrt{A_n^2 + B_n^2}, \quad \sin \alpha_n = \frac{A_n}{H_n}, \quad \cos \alpha_n = \frac{B_n}{H_n}$$

The reader should verify this.

**219.**

$$u(r, t) = 4a^2 \sum_{n=1}^{\infty} \frac{e^{-\gamma_n^2 \frac{t}{a^2}}}{\gamma_n^2 J_0(\gamma_n)} J_0\left(\gamma_n \frac{r}{a}\right),$$

where the $\gamma_n$ are successive positive roots of the equation

$$J_1(\gamma) = 0.$$

**220.**

$$w(r, t) = \sum_{k=1}^{\infty} A_k \frac{J_{\frac{3}{2}}\left(\frac{\mu_k r}{r_0}\right)}{\sqrt{r}} \cos \frac{a\mu_k t}{r_0},$$

where the $\mu_k$ are the positive roots of the equation

$$\mu J'_{\frac{3}{2}}(\mu) - \frac{1}{2} J_{\frac{3}{2}}(\mu) = 0,$$

$$A_k = \frac{2v}{r_0^2 J_{\frac{3}{2}}^2(\mu_k)\left(1 - \frac{2}{\mu_k^2}\right)} \int_0^{r_0} r^{\frac{5}{2}} J_{\frac{3}{2}}\left(\frac{\mu_k r}{r_0}\right) dr =$$

$$= \frac{2vJ_{\frac{5}{2}}\left(\frac{\mu_k}{r_0}\right)}{\mu_k r_0 J_{\frac{3}{2}}(\mu_k)\left(1 - \frac{2}{\mu_k^2}\right)}.$$

**221.** *Procedure*: Let us place the origin of a spherical coordinate system at the center of the vessel and let us direct the $\theta$-axis in the direction of the motion of the vessel for $t < 0$. Then, the potential $u$ of the velocities of the particles of the liquid or gas will depend on the angle $\varphi$ and we have the following boundary-value problem for $u$:

$$\frac{\partial^2 u}{\partial t^2} = a^2 \left\{ \frac{1}{r^2} \frac{\partial}{\partial r}\left(r^2 \frac{\partial u}{\partial r}\right) + \frac{1}{r^2 \sin\theta} \frac{\partial}{\partial \theta}\left(\sin\theta \frac{\partial u}{\partial \theta}\right)\right\},$$

$$(0 \leqslant r \leqslant r_0, \quad 0 \leqslant \theta \leqslant \pi, \quad 0 \leqslant t < \infty),$$

$$u'_r(r_0, \theta, t) = 0,$$

$$u(r, \theta, 0) = vr\cos\theta,$$

$$u'_t(r, \theta, 0) = 0 \qquad (0 \leqslant r \leqslant r_0, \quad 0 \leqslant \theta \leqslant \pi).$$

We should seek a solution of this problem in the form

$$u(r, \theta, t) = w(r, t)\cos\theta.$$

To determine the function $w(r, t)$, we obtain the boundary-value problem of problem 220.

**222.**

$$u(r, t) = \sum_{n=1}^{\infty} \frac{J_0\left(\mu_n \frac{r}{R}\right)}{J_1^2(\mu_n)} \cdot \frac{2}{R^2} \int_0^R r f(r) J_0\left(\mu_n \frac{r}{R}\right) dr e^{-\mu_n^2 \frac{at}{R^2}},$$

where the $\mu_n$ are the positive roots of the equation $J_0(\mu) = 0$. For $f(r) = t_0 = \text{const.}$, we can verify that

$$\frac{2}{R^2} \int_0^R r t_0 J_0\left(\mu_n \frac{r}{R}\right) dr = \frac{2t_0}{\mu_n} J_1(\mu_n).$$

*Hint*: The problem amounts to integrating the equation

$$\frac{\partial u(r,t)}{\partial t}=a^2\left(\frac{\partial^2 u(r,t)}{\partial r^2}+\frac{1}{r}\frac{\partial u(r,t)}{\partial r}\right)\quad (0<r<R,\ t>0)$$

with the conditions

$$u(r,0)=f(r),$$
$$u(R,t)=0,$$
$$\frac{\partial u(0,t)}{\partial r}=0,\qquad u(0,t)<\infty.$$

**224.**

$$\varphi(r,t)=-\frac{a^2P_0}{T\omega^2}\left[1-\frac{J_0\left(\frac{\omega r}{a}\right)}{J_0\left(\frac{\omega R}{a}\right)}\right]\sin\omega t-\\ -\frac{2aP_0\omega R^3}{T}\sum_{n=1}^{\infty}\frac{\sin\frac{\gamma_n at}{R}\,J_0\left(\frac{\gamma_n r}{R}\right)}{\gamma_n^2\left(\omega^2R^2-a^2\gamma_n^2\right)J_0'(\gamma_n)},$$

where the $\gamma_n$ are the successive positive roots of the equation $J_0(\gamma)=0$.

*Procedure*: The problem amounts to integrating the equation

$$\frac{\partial^2\varphi}{\partial r^2}+\frac{1}{r}\frac{\partial\varphi}{\partial r}-\frac{1}{a^2}\frac{\partial^2\varphi}{\partial t^2}=-\frac{P_0\sin\omega t}{T}\qquad (*)$$

with the conditions

$$|\varphi(0,t)|<\infty,\quad \varphi(R,t)=0,$$
$$\varphi(r,0)=0,\qquad \frac{\partial\varphi(r,0)}{\partial t}=0.$$

We seek a solution of this problem in the form of a sum $\varphi=u+v$, where $u$ is a solution of the form $B(r)\sin\omega t$ of the nonhomogeneous equation (*) that satisfies the boundary conditions

$$|u(0,t)|<\infty,\quad u(R,t)=0,$$

and $v$ is the solution of the corresponding homogeneous equation with the conditions

$$|v(0,t)|<\infty,\quad v(R,t)=0,$$
$$v(r,0)=-u(r,0);\qquad \frac{\partial v(r,0)}{\partial t}=-\frac{\partial u(r,0)}{\partial t}.$$

**225.**

$$u(r, t) = \frac{2}{r_0^2} \int_0^{r_0} r [\varphi(r) + t\psi(r)] \, dr + \sum_{n=1}^{\infty} \left( A_n \cos \frac{a\mu_n t}{r_0} + B_n \sin \frac{a\mu_n t}{r_0} \right) J_0 \left( \frac{\mu_n r}{r_0} \right),$$

where

$$A_n = \frac{2}{r_0^2 J_0^2(\mu_n)} \int_0^{r_0} r\varphi(r) J_0 \left( \frac{\mu_n r}{r_0} \right) dr;$$

$$B_n = \frac{2}{a\mu_n r_0 J_0^2(\mu_n)} \int_0^{r_0} r\psi(r) J_0 \left( \frac{\mu_n r}{r_0} \right) dr;$$

$$\varphi(r) = u(r, 0); \quad \psi(r) = u_t'(r, 0)$$

$r_0$ is the radius of the base of the cylinder ($0 \leqslant r \leqslant r_0$) and the $\mu_n$ are the positive roots of the equation $J_1(\mu) = 0$.

*Hint*: The desired potential is a solution of the boundary-value problem

$$\frac{\partial^2 u}{\partial t^2} = a^2 \left( \frac{\partial^2 u}{\partial r^2} + \frac{1}{r} \frac{\partial u}{\partial r} \right) \quad (0 \leqslant r \leqslant r_0, \ 0 < t < \infty),$$

$$|u(0, t)| < \infty, \quad \frac{\partial u(r_0, t)}{\partial t} = 0 \quad (0 < t < \infty),$$

$$u(r, 0) = \varphi(r), \quad u_t'(r, 0) = \psi(r) \quad (0 \leqslant r \leqslant r_0).$$

**226.**

$$u = \begin{cases} \dfrac{u_1 + u_2}{2} + \dfrac{u_1 - u_2}{2} \left[ \dfrac{3}{2} \dfrac{r}{R} P_1(\cos\theta) - \right. \\ \qquad \left. - \dfrac{7}{8} \left( \dfrac{r}{R} \right)^3 P_3(\cos\theta) + \dots \right] \quad (r < R). \\ \dfrac{u_1 + u_2}{2} \dfrac{R}{r} + \dfrac{u_1 - u_2}{2} \left[ \dfrac{3}{2} \left( \dfrac{R}{r} \right)^2 P_1(\cos\theta) - \right. \\ \qquad \left. - \dfrac{7}{8} \left( \dfrac{R}{r} \right)^4 P_3(\cos\theta) + \dots \right] \quad (r > R). \end{cases}$$

*Hint*: Because of the symmetry of the problem, the potential $u$ is independent of the coordinate $\varphi$ and is a function only of the coordinates $r$ and $\theta: u = u(r, \theta)$. The problem amounts to integrating the equation

$$\frac{\partial}{\partial r} \left( r^2 \frac{\partial u}{\partial r} \right) + \frac{1}{\sin\theta} \frac{\partial}{\partial \theta} \left( \sin\theta \frac{\partial u}{\partial \theta} \right) = 0$$

with the boundary condition

$$u|_{r=R}=\begin{cases} u_1 & \text{for} \quad 0\leqslant\theta<\frac{\pi}{2} \\ u_2 & \text{for} \quad \frac{\pi}{2}<\theta\leqslant\pi, \end{cases}$$

where $R$ is the radius of the conductor.

**227.** $U_2=a(x^2-z^2)+b(y^2-z^2)+dxy+eyz+fxz$; $U_3=a\left(x^2y-1/3\,y^3\right)+b\,(x^2z-1/3\,z^3)+c\,(y^2x-1/3\,x^3)+d\,(y^2z-1/3\,z^3)+e\,(z^2x-1/3\,x^3)+f\,(z^2y-1/3\,y^3)+kxyz$, where the coefficients in both polynomials are arbitrary constants.

**228.** The event $B$ consists in having exactly one of the three shots hit the target. The event $C$ consists in having at least two shots hit the target.

**229.** (1) $B+AC$; (2) $AB+AC+BC$; (3) $AB+\bar{A}\bar{B}$; (4) $\bar{A}+\bar{B}$; (5) $\overline{AB}$; (6) $A+B$; (7) $AB$.

**230.** (1) The event is equivalent to the event $A+\bar{A}$, thus, it is certain. (2) The event is impossible.

**231.** 1/720.

**232.** 0.225.

**233.** 0.35.

**234.** 1/30.

**235.** $P_m=\frac{C_M^m C_{N-M}^{n-m}}{C_N^n}$.

**236.** *Solution*: The probability that the first point will not fall in $C$, is $1-\pi R^2/S$, where $S$ is the area of the region $D$. The same holds for the second point, etc. Consequently, the probability that a single point will fall in $C$ is equal to $\left(1-\frac{\pi R^2}{S}\right)^N$.

Therefore, the desired probability is $1-(1-\left(1-\frac{\pi R^2}{S}\right)^N$.

**238.** 20/56; 25/64.

**239.** 0.9.

**240.** 0.45.

**241.** 0.25.

**242.** (a) 1/3; (b) 1/18; (c) 1/3.

**243.** 0.36; 0.91.

**244.** 0.4344.

**245.** 0.142.

**246.** 0.2326.

**247.** *Solution*: Let $P$ denote the probability that the library in question does keep a copy of the book and let $p$ denote the probability that no one else has the book out. Then, the probability that the student will find the book available in one of the three libraries is $1-(1-Pp)^3$. By hypothesis, $P=p=1/2$. Therefore, the probability that he will find the book is $37/64 > 1/2$.

**248.** 0.94.

**250.** 0.48.

**251.** 41/90.

**253.** 7/9; 2/9.

**255.** (1) $\approx$ 0.49; (2) $P_{10}(1) \approx 0.1114$; (3) $\approx 0.9989$; (4) $\approx 0.0091$.

**257.** (1) 243/1024; (2) 405/1024; (3) 270/1024; (4) 1/1024.

**259.**

$$F(x)=P(\xi<x)=\begin{cases} 0 & \text{for} \quad x\leqslant 0, \\ 0{,}8 & \text{for} \quad 0<x\leqslant 1 \\ 1 & \text{for} \quad x>1. \end{cases}$$

**260.** *Hint*: To find the coefficient $a$, we use the property of the probability density that

$$\int_{-\infty}^{\infty} f(x)\,dx=1;$$

$$F(x)=\begin{cases} 0 \quad \text{for} \quad x<-\frac{\pi}{2}, \\ \frac{1}{2}\sin(x+1) \quad \text{for} \quad -\frac{\pi}{2}<x<\frac{\pi}{2} \\ 0 \quad \text{for} \quad x>\frac{\pi}{2}. \end{cases}$$

$$P\left(0<\xi<\frac{\pi}{4}\right)=F\left(\frac{\pi}{4}\right)-F(0)=\frac{\sqrt{2}}{4}.$$

**261.** $P(-1<\xi<1)=0.5$.

**263.**

$$1\cdot\frac{1}{2}+2\cdot\frac{1}{2^2}+3\frac{1}{2^3}+\dots= \\ =\frac{1}{2}\left(1+\frac{1}{2}+\frac{1}{2^2}+\dots\right)^2=2$$

**264.** 150 v.

**266.** 0.6.

**269.** $M\xi=\frac{\alpha+\beta}{2}$; $D\xi=\frac{1}{12}(\beta-\alpha)^2$.

**270.** $M\xi=\frac{1}{p}$; $D\xi=\frac{q}{p^2}$; $\sigma\xi=\frac{\sqrt{q}}{p}$ $(q=1-p)$.

**271.**

$$M\left(\frac{\pi d^2}{4}\right)=\frac{\pi}{12}(b^2+ab+a^2);\ D\left(\frac{\pi d^2}{4}\right)=\frac{\pi^2}{16}D(d^2)=$$
$$=\frac{\pi^2}{16}[Md^4-(Md^2)^2]=\frac{\pi^2}{720}(b-a)^2(4b^2+7ab+4a^2).$$

**272.** (1) 0.68269; (2) 0.95450; (3) 0.99730.

**273.** (a) $Ms=4\sqrt{\frac{a^3}{\pi}}\int\limits_0^\infty s^3e^{-aS^2}\,ds=\frac{2}{\sqrt{\pi a}}=2\sqrt{\frac{2kT}{\pi m}}$; (b) the energy of a molecule $E=ms^2/2$, so that

$$ME=\int\limits_0^\infty \frac{1}{2}ms^2p(s)\,ds=\frac{3}{2}kT.$$

**274.** $P(\alpha<\xi<\beta)=\frac{1}{2}\left\{\Phi\left(\frac{\beta-a}{\sigma}\right)-\Phi\left(\frac{\alpha-a}{\sigma}\right)\right\}$, where

$$\Phi(x)=\frac{2}{\sqrt{2\pi}}\int\limits_0^\infty e^{-\frac{z^2}{2}}\,dz;\ P(5<\xi<10)=0.0214.$$

**275.** $P(|\xi-a|<l)=\Phi\left(\frac{l}{\sigma}\right)$. The value of the function $\Phi(x)$ is given in the answer to problem 274.

**276.** (1) The mean value of the variable $x$ is

$$Mx=\int\limits_0^\infty xw(x)\,dx=2\sqrt{\frac{Dt}{\pi}}e^{-C^2}+\frac{2x_0}{\sqrt{\pi}}\int\limits_0^C e^{-x^2}\,dx,$$

where

$$C=\frac{x_0}{2\sqrt{Dt}};$$

(2) $M(x^2)=\int\limits_0^\infty x^2w(x)\,dx=\frac{1}{\sqrt{\pi}}\left[\int\limits_{-C}^\infty (x_0+2\sqrt{Dt}\cdot\xi)^2e^{-\xi^2}\,d\xi+\right.$
$\left.\int\limits_C^\infty(-x_0+2\sqrt{Dt}\xi)^2e^{-\xi^2}\,d\xi\right]=\frac{1}{\sqrt{\pi}}\left[2x_0^2\int\limits_0^\infty e^{-\xi^2}\,d\xi+8Dt\int\limits_0^\infty \xi^2e^{-\xi^2}\,d\xi\right]=$
$x_0^2+2Dt$; and the desired variance is $Dx=M(x^2)-(Mx)^2$;

(3) The mean value of the displacement $x-x_0$ is

$$M(x-x_0)=2\sqrt{\frac{Dt}{\pi}}e^{-C^2}-\frac{2x_0}{\sqrt{\pi}}\int\limits_0^\infty e^{-x^2}\,dx;$$

(4) The mean value of the square of the displacement is

$$M(x-x_0)^2 = 2Dt - 4x_0\sqrt{\frac{Dt}{\pi}}\, e^{-C^2} + \frac{4x_0^2}{\sqrt{\pi}}\int_0^{\infty} e^{-x^2}\,dx$$

**277.**

$$M(\xi\cdot\eta) = \frac{a+b}{2}\cdot\frac{c+d}{2};$$

$$D(\xi\cdot\eta) = \frac{a^2+ab+b^2}{3}\cdot\frac{c^2+cd+d^2}{3} - \frac{(a+b)^2}{4}\,\frac{(c+d)^2}{4}$$

*Hint*: Use the formula

$$D(\xi\cdot\eta) = M(\xi^2\eta^2) - [M(\xi\eta)]^2 = M\xi^2 M\eta^2 - (M\xi)^2(M\eta)^2$$

**279.** 0.866.

**280.** *Procedure*: The problem consists in finding a number $a > 0$ such that

$$P(|x-\bar{x}| < a) > 0{,}95$$

We obtain $a > 0.394$; that is, with probability exceeding 0.95, we may guarantee that the deviation of the length will not exceed approximately 0.4 cm.

**281.** $\approx$ 0.665. *Procedure*: The probable deviation (or the "mean deviation" or "mean error") is defined as one-half the length of the interval symmetrically located about the center of dispersion the probability of falling within which is equal to 1/2. It can be shown that if $x$, $y$, and $z$ are mutually independent random variables obeying a normal law, the probable deviation of the variable $u = x+y+z$ is equal to

$$E_u = \sqrt{E_x^2 + E_y^2 + E_z^2}$$

where $E_x$, $E_y$, and $E_z$ are the probable deviations of $x$, $y$, and $z$ respectively. In the present problem, the deviation of the total error is $\sqrt{28^2+8^2+12^2} = 28$ м.

**282.** $M\xi = a$; $D\xi = a^2$;

$$F(x) = \begin{cases} 0, & \text{if} \quad x < 0 \\ 1 - e^{-\frac{x}{a}}, & \text{if} \quad x > 0 \end{cases}$$

**283.** $\approx$ 4%.

**285.** $\approx$ 0.00206. *Hint*: Use Laplace's asymptotic local theorem:

$$P_n(m) \approx \frac{1}{\sqrt{2\pi npq}}\, e^{-\frac{1}{2}\left(\frac{m-np}{\sqrt{npq}}\right)^2}$$

to obtain

$$\frac{1}{\sqrt{2\pi npq}} = \frac{1}{\sqrt{2\pi}} : \sqrt{npq} = \frac{0.3989}{\sqrt{npq}}$$

**286.** *Hint*: Use Laplace's local theorem (see hint to problem 285). Since $n=50, p=0.4, q=0.6$, and $m=25$, the desired probability is

$$P_{50}(25) = \frac{0.3989}{\sqrt{50\cdot 0.4\cdot 0.6}} e^{-\frac{25}{2\cdot 50\cdot 0.4\cdot 0.6}} \approx 0.115e^{-1.042} \approx 0.041$$

**287.** *Solution*: Use Laplace's integral theorem to obtain

$$P(m \leqslant 70) = P\left(-\frac{50}{\sqrt{49.75}} \leqslant \frac{m-np}{\sqrt{npq}} \leqslant \frac{20}{\sqrt{49.75}}\right) =$$

$$= P\left(-7.09 \leqslant \frac{m-np}{\sqrt{npq}} \leqslant 2.84\right) \approx \frac{1}{\sqrt{2\pi}} \int_{-7.09}^{2.84} e^{-\frac{t^2}{2}} dt = 0.9975.$$

**288.** 0.82.

**289.** (a) $P_{10}(8) = C_{10}^{8}\left(\frac{3}{4}\right)^{8}\left(\frac{1}{4}\right)^{2} \approx 0.2816$. Since $n$ is small, use of the formula

$$P_n(m) \approx \frac{1}{\sqrt{2\pi npq}} e^{-\frac{(m-np)^2}{2npq}}$$

gives the crude result: $\approx 0.2724$.

(b) Since the given bounds (70 and 80) differ from $np = 75$ by the same amount, we use Laplace's approximate integral formula in the form

$$P_n(a < m < b) \approx \frac{1}{\sqrt{2\pi}} \int_{-t}^{t} e^{-\frac{z^2}{2}} dz = \Phi(t).$$

In the present case, $a=70$, $b=80$, $t = \frac{np-a}{\sqrt{npq}} = \frac{2}{\sqrt{3}}$, so that the desired probability is

$$P_{100}(70 < m < 80) \approx \Phi\left(\frac{2}{\sqrt{3}}\right) \approx 0.7518.$$

(c) $$\sum_{m=81}^{100} P_{100}(m) \approx 0.5 - \Phi\left(\frac{2}{\sqrt{3}}\right) \approx 0.1241.$$

(d) $\sum_{m=0}^{70} P_{100}(m) \approx \Phi\left(-\frac{2}{\sqrt{3}}\right) + 0.5 \approx 0.1241.$

(e) $\Phi\left(\frac{0.035 \cdot \sqrt{400}}{\sqrt{0.75 \cdot 0.25}}\right) \approx \Phi(1.62) = 0.8948.$

**290.** (1) $P_{150}(78 < m < 102) = \Phi(2) = 0.9545.$
(2) $P_{150}(78 < m < 108) = 0.9759.$

**295.** 0.0408. *Hint*: Use Laplace's local theorem.

**296.** *Solution*: We divide the interval $t$ into a large number of small subintervals $\Delta t$. Obviously, in case (1), there will not be any calls at all in the interval $t$ if there are no calls in the subintervals. Therefore, the probability $P_0(t)$ that there will be no calls in the interval $t$ is equal to the product of the analogous probabilities $P_0(\Delta t)$ for the subintervals $\Delta t$:

$$P_0(t) = [P_0(\Delta t)]^{\frac{t}{\Delta t}},$$

where $t/\Delta t$ is the number of intervals. If $q(\Delta t)$ is the probability that a call will be made during an interval $\Delta t$, the preceding equation can be written in the form

$$P_0(t) = (1-q)^{\frac{t}{\Delta t}}.$$

Therefore,

$$\ln P_0(t) = \frac{t}{\Delta t} \ln(1-q)$$

and, for small $q$, $\ln(1-q) \approx -q$. Therefore,

$$\ln P_0(t) = -\frac{tq}{\Delta t} \equiv -kt,$$

so that

$$P_0(t) = e^{-kt}.$$

In case (2), we take an interval of length $t$ and, abutting it on the right, a small interval $\Delta t$. Together, they form an interval $t+\Delta t$. If $n$ calls are made in this interval, either all will occur in $t$ and none in $\Delta t$ or $n-1$ will occur in $t$ and one in $\Delta t$. In all other cases, more than one call will occur in the interval $\Delta t$. Since these cases are very unlikely, we may neglect them. The probability of $n$ calls in the interval $t+\Delta t$ is equal to

$$P_n(t+\Delta t) = P_n(t)(1-k\,\Delta t) + P_{n-1}(t)\,k\,\Delta t$$

(Here, we use the theorems on the multiplication and addition of probabilities.) This last relation can easily be reduced to the recursion differential equation (letting $\Delta t \to 0$):

$$\frac{dP_n}{dt} = k(P_{n-1} - P_n)$$

for the desired probability $P_n$. For $n = 1$, we obtain the equation

$$\frac{dP_1}{dt} + kP_1 = kP_0 \equiv ke^{-kt},$$

where

$$P_1 = (c_1 + kt)\, e^{-kt}.$$

The constant $c_1$ is determined from the conditions that $P_1 \to 0$ as $t \to 0$. From this, we obtain

$$P_1 = kte^{-kt}.$$

Analogously, we find

$$P_2 = \frac{(kt)^2}{2!}\, e^{-kt}.$$

Obviously, in general,

$$P_n = \frac{(kt)^n}{n!}\, e^{-kt}.$$

**297.** The number of electrons flying off the cathode in the interval $\Delta t$ is distributed according to a Poisson law:

$$P_m = \frac{(n\,\Delta t)^m}{m!}\, e^{-n\,\Delta t}.$$

**298.** $P_N(n) = \frac{\bar{n}^n}{n!} e^{-\bar{n}}$; $\overline{n^2} - \bar{n}^2 = \bar{n}$.

**299.** $P_n(m) = \frac{\left(\frac{n}{60}\right)^m}{m!} e^{-\frac{n}{60}}$.

**300.** $P_n(m) = \frac{\left(n\frac{v}{V}\right)^m}{m!} e^{-\frac{nv}{V}}$.

**301.** $P(|\xi - M\xi| < \varepsilon) > 1 - \frac{D\xi}{\varepsilon^2}$.

**302.** $P(|\xi - M\xi| \leqslant 0.5 \geqslant 0.6$, where $\xi$ is the length of the object.

**304.** Yes, since the hypotheses of Chebyshev's theorem are satisfied:

$$M\xi_n = 0, \quad M\xi_n^2 = \alpha^2, \quad D\xi_n = \alpha^2.$$

**306.** *Hint*: Apply Chebyshev's inequality to the quantity

$$Y = \frac{\sum_{i=1}^{n} x_i}{n}$$

# Appendices

# APPENDIX I

**Table of Values of Bessel Functions**

| $x$ | $J_0(x)$ | $J_1(x)$ | $Y_0(x)$ | $Y_1(x)$ | $I_0(x)$ | $I_1(x)$ |
|---|---|---|---|---|---|---|
| 0.0 | +1.0000 | 0.0000 | $-\infty$ | $-\infty$ | +1.000 | 0.0000 |
| 0.1 | 0.9975 | +0.0499 | −1.5342 | −6.4589 | 1.003 | +0.0501 |
| 0.2 | 0.9900 | 0.0995 | 1.0811 | 3.3238 | 1.010 | 0.1005 |
| 0.3 | 0.9776 | 0.1483 | 0.8073 | 2.2931 | 1.023 | 0.1517 |
| 0.4 | 0.9604 | 0.1960 | 0.6060 | 1.7809 | 1.040 | 0.2040 |
| 0.5 | +0.9385 | +0.2423 | −0.4445 | −1.4715 | 1.063 | 0.2579 |
| 0.6 | 0.9120 | 0.2867 | 0.3085 | 1.2604 | 1.092 | 0.3137 |
| 0.7 | 0.8812 | 0.3290 | 0.1907 | 1.1032 | 1.126 | 0.3719 |
| 0.8 | 0.8463 | 0.3688 | −0.0868 | 0.9781 | 1.167 | 0.4329 |
| 0.9 | 0.8075 | 0.4059 | +0.0056 | 0.8731 | 1.213 | 0.4971 |
| 1.0 | +0.7652 | +0.4401 | +0.0883 | −0.7812 | 1.266 | 0.5652 |
| 1.1 | 0.7196 | 0.4709 | 0.1622 | 0.6981 | 1.326 | 0.6375 |
| 1.2 | 0.6711 | 0.4983 | 0.2281 | 0.6211 | 1.394 | 0.7147 |
| 1.3 | 0.6201 | 0.5220 | 0.2865 | 0.5485 | 1.469 | 0.7973 |
| 1.4 | 0.5669 | 0.5419 | 0.3379 | 0.4791 | 1.553 | 0.8861 |
| 1.5 | +0.5118 | +0.5579 | +0.3824 | −0.4123 | 1.647 | 0.9817 |
| 1.6 | 0.4554 | 0.5699 | 0.4204 | 0.3476 | 1.750 | 1.085 |
| 1.7 | 0.3980 | 0.5778 | 0.4520 | 0.2847 | 1.864 | 1.196 |
| 1.8 | 0.3400 | 0.5815 | 0.4774 | 0.2237 | 1.990 | 1.317 |
| 1.9 | 0.2818 | 0.5812 | 0.4968 | 0.1644 | 2.128 | 1.448 |
| 2.0 | +0.2239 | +0.5767 | +0.5104 | −0.1070 | 2.280 | 1.591 |
| 2.1 | 0.1666 | 0.5683 | 0.5183 | −0.0517 | 2.446 | 1.745 |
| 2.2 | 0.1104 | 0.5560 | 0.5208 | +0.0015 | 2.629 | 1.914 |
| 2.3 | 0.0555 | 0.5399 | 0.5181 | 0.0523 | 2.830 | 2.098 |
| 2.4 | 0.0025 | 0.5202 | 0.5104 | 0.1005 | 3.049 | 2.298 |
| 2.5 | −0.0484 | +0.4971 | +0.4981 | +0.1459 | 3.290 | 2.517 |
| 2.6 | 0.0968 | 0.4708 | 0.4813 | 0.1884 | 3.553 | 2.755 |
| 2.7 | 0.1424 | 0.4416 | 0.4605 | 0.2276 | 3.842 | 3.016 |
| 2.8 | 0.1850 | 0.4097 | 0.4359 | 0.2635 | 4.157 | 3.301 |
| 2.9 | 0.2243 | 0.3754 | 0.4079 | 0.2959 | 4.503 | 3.613 |
| 3.0 | −0.2601 | +0.3391 | +0.3768 | +0.3247 | 4.881 | 3.953 |
| 3.1 | 0.2921 | 0.3009 | 0.3431 | 0.3496 | 5.294 | 4.326 |
| 3.2 | 0.3202 | 0.2613 | 0.3070 | 0.3707 | 5.747 | 4.734 |
| 3.3 | 0.3443 | 0.2207 | 0.2691 | 0.3878 | 6.243 | 5.181 |
| 3.4 | 0.3643 | 0.1792 | 0.2296 | 0.4010 | 6.785 | 5.670 |

**Appendix I (Continued)**

| $x$ | $J_0(x)$ | $J_1(x)$ | $Y_0(x)$ | $Y_1(x)$ | $I_0(x)$ | $I_1(x)$ |
|---|---|---|---|---|---|---|
| 3.5 | −0.3801 | −0.1374 | +0.1890 | +0.4102 | 7.378 | 6.206 |
| 3.6 | 0.3918 | 0.0955 | 0.1477 | 0.4154 | 8.028 | 6.793 |
| 3.7 | 0.3992 | 0.0538 | 0.1061 | 0.4167 | 8.739 | 7.436 |
| 3.8 | 0.4026 | 0.0128 | 0.6450 | 0.4141 | 9.517 | 8.140 |
| 3.9 | 0.4018 | 0.0272 | 0.2338 | 0.4078 | 10.37 | 8.913 |
| 4.0 | −0.3971 | −0.0660 | −0.0169 | +0.3979 | 11.30 | 9.759 |
| 4.1 | 0.3887 | 0.1033 | 0.0561 | 0.3846 | 12.32 | 10.69 |
| 4.2 | 0.3766 | 0.1386 | 0.0937 | 0.3680 | 13.44 | 11.71 |
| 4.3 | 0.3610 | 0.1719 | 0.1296 | 0.3484 | 14.67 | 12.82 |
| 4.4 | 0.3423 | 0.2028 | 0.1633 | 0.3260 | 16.01 | 14.05 |
| 4.5 | −0.3205 | −0.2311 | −0.1947 | +0.3010 | 17.48 | 15.39 |
| 4.6 | 0.2961 | 0.2566 | 0.2235 | 0.2737 | 19.09 | 16.86 |
| 4.7 | 0.2693 | 0.2791 | 0.2494 | 0.2445 | 20.86 | 18.48 |
| 4.8 | 0.2404 | 0.2985 | 0.2723 | 0.2136 | 22.79 | 20.25 |
| 4.9 | 0.2097 | 0.3147 | 0.2920 | 0.1812 | 24.91 | 22.20 |
| 5.0 | −0.1776 | −0.3276 | −0.3085 | +0.1479 | 27.24 | 24.34 |
| 5.1 | 0.1443 | 0.3371 | 0.3216 | 0.1137 | 29.79 | 26.68 |
| 5.2 | 0.1103 | 0.3432 | 0.3312 | 0.0792 | 32.58 | 29.25 |
| 5.3 | 0.0758 | 0.3460 | 0.3374 | 0.0445 | 35.65 | 32.08 |
| 5.4 | 0.0412 | 0.3453 | 0.3402 | +0.0101 | 39.01 | 35.18 |
| 5.5 | −0.0068 | −0.3414 | −0.3395 | −0.0238 | 42.69 | 38.59 |
| 5.6 | +0.0270 | 0.3343 | 0.3354 | 0.0568 | 46.74 | 42.33 |
| 5.7 | 0.0599 | 0.3241 | 0.3282 | 0.0887 | 51.17 | 46.44 |
| 5.8 | 0.0917 | 0.3110 | 0.3177 | 0.1192 | 56.04 | 50.95 |
| 5.9 | 0.1220 | 0.2951 | 0.3044 | 0.1481 | 61.38 | 55.90 |
| 6.0 | +0.1506 | −0.2767 | −0.2882 | −0.1750 | 67.23 | 61.34 |
| 6.1 | 0.1773 | 0.2559 | 0.2694 | 0.1998 | 73.66 | 67.32 |
| 6.2 | 0.2017 | 0.2329 | 0.2483 | 0.2223 | 80.72 | 73.89 |
| 6.3 | 0.2238 | 0.2081 | 0.2251 | 0.2422 | 88.46 | 81.10 |
| 6.4 | 0.2433 | 0.1816 | 0.1999 | 0.2596 | 96.96 | 89.03 |
| 6.5 | +0.2601 | −0.1538 | −0.1732 | −0.2741 | 106.3 | 97.73 |
| 6.6 | 0.2740 | 0.1250 | 0.1452 | 0.2857 | 116.5 | 107.3 |
| 6.7 | 0.2851 | 0.0953 | 0.1162 | 0.2945 | 127.8 | 117.8 |
| 6.8 | 0.2931 | 0.0652 | 0.0864 | 0.3002 | 140.1 | 129.4 |
| 6.9 | 0.2981 | 0.0349 | 0.0562 | 0.3029 | 153.7 | 142.1 |
| 7.0 | +0.3001 | −0.0047 | −0.0259 | −0.3027 | 168.6 | 156.0 |
| 7.1 | 0.2991 | +0.0252 | +0.0042 | 0.2995 | 184.9 | 171.4 |
| 7.2 | 0.2951 | 0.0543 | 0.0338 | 0.2934 | 202.9 | 188.2 |
| 7.3 | 0.2882 | 0.0826 | 0.0628 | 0.2846 | 222.7 | 206.8 |
| 7.4 | 0.2786 | 0.1096 | 0.0907 | 0.2731 | 244.3 | 227.2 |
| 7.5 | +0.2663 | +0.1352 | +0.1173 | −0.2591 | 268.2 | 249.6 |
| 7.6 | 0.2516 | 0.1592 | 0.1424 | 0.2428 | 294.3 | 274.2 |
| 7.7 | 0.2346 | 0.1813 | 0.1658 | 0.2243 | 323.1 | 301.3 |
| 7.8 | 0.2154 | 0.2014 | 0.1872 | 0.2039 | 354.7 | 331.1 |
| 7.9 | 0.1944 | 0.2192 | 0.2065 | 0.1817 | 389.4 | 363.8 |

**Appendix I (Continued)**

| $x$ | $J_0(x)$ | $J_1(x)$ | $Y_0(x)$ | $Y_1(x)$ | $I_0(x)$ | $I_1(x)$ |
|---|---|---|---|---|---|---|
| 8.0 | +0.1717 | +0.2346 | +0.2235 | −0.1581 | 427.6 | 399.9 |
| 8.1 | 0.1475 | 0.2476 | 0.2381 | 0.1331 | 469.5 | 439.5 |
| 8.2 | 0.1222 | 0.2580 | 0.2501 | 0.1072 | 515.6 | 483.0 |
| 8.3 | 0.0960 | 0.2657 | 0.2595 | 0.0806 | 566.3 | 531.0 |
| 8.4 | 0.0692 | 0.2708 | 0.2662 | 0.0535 | 621.9 | 583.7 |
| 8.5 | +0.0419 | +0.2731 | +0.2702 | −0.0262 | 683.2 | 641.6 |
| 8.6 | +0.0146 | 0.2728 | 0.2715 | +0.0011 | 750.5 | 705.4 |
| 8.7 | −0.0125 | 0.2697 | 0.2700 | 0.0280 | 824.4 | 775.5 |
| 8.8 | 0.0392 | 0.2641 | 0.2659 | 0.0544 | 905.8 | 852.7 |
| 8.9 | 0.0653 | 0.2559 | 0.2592 | 0.0799 | 995.2 | 937.5 |
| 9.0 | −0.0903 | +0.2453 | +0.2499 | +0.1043 | 1094 | 1031 |
| 9.1 | 0.1142 | 0.2324 | 0.2383 | 0.1275 | 1202 | 1134 |
| 9.2 | 0.1367 | 0.2174 | 0.2245 | 0.1491 | 1321 | 1247 |
| 9.3 | 0.1577 | 0.2004 | 0.2086 | 0.1691 | 1451 | 1371 |
| 9.4 | 0.1768 | 0.1816 | 0.1907 | 0.1871 | 1595 | 1508 |
| 9.5 | −0.1939 | +0.1613 | +0.1712 | +0.2032 | 1753 | 1658 |
| 9.6 | 0.2090 | 0.1395 | 0.1502 | 0.2171 | 1927 | 1824 |
| 9.7 | 0.2218 | 0.1166 | 0.1279 | 0.2287 | 2119 | 2006 |
| 9.8 | 0.2323 | 0.0928 | 0.1045 | 0.2379 | 2329 | 2207 |
| 9.9 | 0.2403 | 0.0684 | 0.0804 | 0.2447 | 2561 | 2428 |
| 10.0 | −0.2459 | +0.0435 | +0.0557 | +0.2490 | 2816 | 2671 |

# APPENDIX II

**Table of Roots of the Equations $J_0(x) = 0$, $J_1(x) = 0$**

| $k$ | $\mu_k$ | $J_1(\mu_k)$ | $\mu_{1,k}$ | $J_0(\mu_{1,k})$ |
|---|---|---|---|---|
| 1 | 2.405 | +0.5191 | 3.832 | −0.4028 |
| 2 | 5.520 | −0.3403 | 7.016 | +0.3001 |
| 3 | 8.654 | +0.2715 | 10.17 | −0.2497 |
| 4 | 11.79 | −0.2325 | 13.32 | +0.2184 |
| 5 | 14.93 | +0.2065 | 16.47 | −0.1965 |
| 6 | 18.07 | −0.1877 | 19.62 | +0.1801 |
| 7 | 21.21 | +0.1733 | 22.76 | −0.1672 |
| 8 | 24.35 | −0.1617 | 25.90 | +0.1567 |
| 9 | 27.49 | +0.1522 | 29.05 | −0.1480 |
| 10 | 30.63 | −0.1442 | 32.19 | +0.1406 |

# APPENDIX III

**Table of Values of the Function** $\varphi(t) = \frac{1}{\sqrt{2\pi}} e^{-\frac{t^2}{2}}$

| 1 | 0 | 1 | 2 | 3 | 4 | 5 | 6 | 7 | 8 | 9 |
|---|---|---|---|---|---|---|---|---|---|---|
| 0.0 | 3989 | 3989 | 3989 | 3988 | 3986 | 3984 | 3982 | 3980 | 3977 | 3973 |
| 0.1 | 3970 | 3965 | 3961 | 3956 | 3951 | 3945 | 3939 | 3932 | 3925 | 3918 |
| 0.2 | 3910 | 3902 | 3894 | 3885 | 3876 | 3867 | 3857 | 3847 | 3836 | 3825 |
| 0.3 | 3814 | 3802 | 3790 | 3778 | 3765 | 3752 | 3739 | 3725 | 3712 | 3697 |
| 0.4 | 3683 | 3668 | 3653 | 3637 | 3621 | 3605 | 3589 | 3572 | 3555 | 3538 |
| 0.5 | 3521 | 3503 | 3485 | 3467 | 3448 | 3429 | 3410 | 3391 | 3372 | 3352 |
| 0.6 | 3332 | 3312 | 3292 | 3271 | 3251 | 3230 | 3209 | 3187 | 3166 | 3144 |
| 0.7 | 3123 | 3101 | 3079 | 3056 | 3034 | 3011 | 2989 | 2966 | 2943 | 2920 |
| 0.8 | 2897 | 2874 | 2850 | 2827 | 2803 | 2780 | 2756 | 2732 | 2709 | 2685 |
| 0.9 | 2661 | 2637 | 2613 | 2589 | 2565 | 2541 | 2516 | 2492 | 2468 | 2444 |
| 1.0 | 2420 | 2396 | 2371 | 2347 | 2323 | 2299 | 2275 | 2251 | 2227 | 2203 |
| 1.1 | 2179 | 2155 | 2131 | 2107 | 2083 | 2059 | 2036 | 2012 | 1989 | 1965 |
| 1.2 | 1942 | 1919 | 1895 | 1872 | 1849 | 1826 | 1804 | 1781 | 1758 | 1736 |
| 1.3 | 1714 | 1691 | 1669 | 1647 | 1626 | 1604 | 1582 | 1561 | 1539 | 1518 |
| 1.4 | 1497 | 1476 | 1456 | 1435 | 1415 | 1394 | 1374 | 1354 | 1334 | 1315 |
| 1.5 | 1295 | 1276 | 1257 | 1238 | 1219 | 1200 | 1182 | 1163 | 1145 | 1127 |
| 1.6 | 1109 | 1092 | 1074 | 1057 | 1040 | 1023 | 1006 | 0989 | 0973 | 0957 |
| 1.7 | 0940 | 0925 | 0909 | 0893 | 0878 | 0863 | 0848 | 0833 | 0818 | 0804 |
| 1.8 | 0790 | 0775 | 0761 | 0748 | 0734 | 0721 | 0707 | 0694 | 0681 | 0669 |
| 1.9 | 0656 | 0644 | 0632 | 0620 | 0608 | 0596 | 0584 | 0573 | 0562 | 0551 |
| 2.0 | 0540 | 0529 | 0519 | 0508 | 0498 | 0488 | 0478 | 0468 | 0459 | 0449 |
| 2.1 | 0440 | 0431 | 0422 | 0413 | 0404 | 0396 | 0387 | 0379 | 0371 | 0363 |
| 2.2 | 0855 | 0347 | 0339 | 0332 | 0325 | 0317 | 0310 | 0303 | 0297 | 0290 |
| 2.3 | 0283 | 0277 | 0270 | 0264 | 0258 | 0252 | 0246 | 0241 | 0235 | 0229 |
| 2.4 | 0224 | 0219 | 0213 | 0203 | 0203 | 0198 | 0194 | 0189 | 0184 | 0180 |
| 2.5 | 0175 | 0171 | 0167 | 0163 | 0158 | 0154 | 0151 | 0147 | 0143 | 0139 |
| 2.6 | 0136 | 0132 | 0129 | 0126 | 0122 | 0119 | 0116 | 0113 | 0110 | 0107 |
| 2.7 | 0104 | 0101 | 0099 | 0096 | 0093 | 0091 | 0088 | 0086 | 0084 | 0081 |
| 2.8 | 0079 | 0077 | 0075 | 0073 | 0071 | 0069 | 0067 | 0065 | 0063 | 0061 |
| 2.9 | 0060 | 0058 | 0056 | 0055 | 0053 | 0051 | 0050 | 0048 | 0047 | 0046 |
| 3.0 | 0044 | 0043 | 0042 | 0040 | 0039 | 0038 | 0037 | 0036 | 0035 | 0034 |
| 4.0 | 0001 | 0001 | 0001 | 0000 | 0000 | 0000 | 0000 | 0000 | 0000 | 0000 |

# APPENDIX IV

**Table of Values of the Function** $F(t) = \frac{2}{\sqrt{\pi}} \int_0^t e^{-\frac{s^2}{2}} ds$

**for different values of** $t$

| $t$ | $F(t)$ | $t$ | $F(t)$ | $t$ | $F(t)$ | $t$ | $F(t)$ |
|---|---|---|---|---|---|---|---|
| 0.00 | 0.00000 | 0.30 | 0.23582 | 0.60 | 0.45149 | 0.90 | 0.63188 |
| 01 | 00798 | 31 | 24344 | 61 | 45814 | 91 | 63718 |
| 02 | 01596 | 32 | 25103 | 62 | 46474 | 92 | 64243 |
| 03 | 02393 | 33 | 25860 | 63 | 47131 | 93 | 64763 |
| 04 | 03191 | 34 | 26614 | 64 | 47783 | 94 | 65278 |
| 05 | 03988 | 35 | 27366 | 65 | 48431 | 95 | 65789 |
| 06 | 04784 | 36 | 28115 | 66 | 49075 | 96 | 66294 |
| 07 | 05581 | 37 | 28862 | 67 | 49714 | 97 | 66795 |
| 08 | 06376 | 38 | 29605 | 68 | 50350 | 98 | 67291 |
| 09 | 07171 | 39 | 30346 | 69 | 50981 | 99 | 67783 |
| 0.10 | 0.07966 | 0.40 | 0.31084 | 0.70 | 0.51607 | 1.00 | 0.68269 |
| 11 | 08759 | 41 | 31819 | 71 | 52230 | 01 | 68750 |
| 12 | 09552 | 42 | 32552 | 72 | 52848 | 02 | 69227 |
| 13 | 10348 | 43 | 33280 | 73 | 53461 | 03 | 69699 |
| 14 | 11134 | 44 | 34006 | 74 | 54070 | 04 | 70166 |
| 15 | 11924 | 45 | 34729 | 75 | 54675 | 05 | 70628 |
| 16 | 12712 | 46 | 35448 | 76 | 55275 | 06 | 71086 |
| 17 | 13499 | 47 | 36164 | 77 | 55870 | 07 | 71538 |
| 18 | 14285 | 48 | 36877 | 78 | 56461 | 08 | 71986 |
| 19 | 15069 | 49 | 37587 | 79 | 57047 | 09 | 72429 |
| 0.20 | 0.15852 | 0.50 | 0.38292 | 0.80 | 0.57629 | 1.10 | 0.72867 |
| 21 | 16633 | 51 | 38995 | 81 | 58206 | 11 | 73300 |
| 22 | 17413 | 52 | 39694 | 82 | 58778 | 12 | 73729 |
| 23 | 18191 | 53 | 40389 | 83 | 59346 | 13 | 74152 |
| 24 | 18967 | 54 | 41080 | 84 | 59909 | 14 | 74571 |
| 25 | 19741 | 55 | 41768 | 85 | 60468 | 15 | 74986 |
| 26 | 20514 | 56 | 42452 | 86 | 61021 | 16 | 75395 |
| 27 | 21284 | 57 | 43132 | 87 | 61570 | 17 | 75800 |
| 28 | 22052 | 58 | 43809 | 88 | 62114 | 18 | 76200 |
| 29 | 22818 | 59 | 44481 | 89 | 62653 | 19 | 76595 |

**Appendix IV (Continued)**

| $t$ | $F(t)$ | $t$ | $F(t)$ | $t$ | $F(t)$ | $t$ | $F(t)$ |
|---|---|---|---|---|---|---|---|
| 1.20 | 0.76986 | 1.70 | 0.91087 | 2.20 | 0.97219 | 2.70 | 0.99307 |
| 21 | 77372 | 71 | 91273 | 21 | 97289 | 71 | 99327 |
| 22 | 77754 | 72 | 91457 | 22 | 97358 | 72 | 99347 |
| 23 | 78130 | 73 | 91637 | 23 | 97425 | 73 | 99367 |
| 24 | 78502 | 74 | 91814 | 24 | 97491 | 74 | 99386 |
| 25 | 78870 | 75 | 91988 | 25 | 97555 | 75 | 99404 |
| 26 | 79233 | 76 | 92159 | 26 | 97618 | 76 | 99422 |
| 27 | 79592 | 77 | 92327 | 27 | 97679 | 77 | 99439 |
| 28 | 79945 | 78 | 92492 | 28 | 97739 | 78 | 99456 |
| 29 | 80295 | 79 | 92655 | 29 | 97798 | 79 | 99473 |
| 1.30 | 0.80640 | 1.80 | 0.92814 | 2.30 | 0.97855 | 2.80 | 0.99489 |
| 31 | 80980 | 81 | 92970 | 31 | 97911 | 81 | 99505 |
| 32 | 81316 | 82 | 93124 | 32 | 97966 | 82 | 99520 |
| 33 | 81648 | 83 | 93275 | 33 | 98019 | 83 | 99535 |
| 34 | 81975 | 84 | 93423 | 34 | 98072 | 84 | 99549 |
| 35 | 82298 | 85 | 93569 | 35 | 98123 | 85 | 99563 |
| 36 | 82617 | 86 | 93711 | 36 | 98172 | 86 | 99576 |
| 37 | 82931 | 87 | 93852 | 37 | 98221 | 87 | 99590 |
| 38 | 83241 | 88 | 93989 | 38 | 98269 | 88 | 99602 |
| 39 | 83547 | 89 | 94124 | 39 | 98315 | 89 | 99615 |
| 1.40 | 0.83849 | 1.90 | 0.94257 | 2.40 | 0.98360 | 2.90 | 0.99627 |
| 41 | 84146 | 91 | 94387 | 41 | 98405 | 91 | 99639 |
| 42 | 84439 | 92 | 94514 | 42 | 98448 | 92 | 99650 |
| 43 | 84728 | 93 | 94639 | 43 | 98490 | 93 | 99661 |
| 44 | 85013 | 94 | 94762 | 44 | 98531 | 94 | 99672 |
| 45 | 85294 | 95 | 94882 | 45 | 98571 | 95 | 99682 |
| 46 | 85571 | 96 | 95000 | 46 | 98611 | 96 | 99692 |
| 47 | 85844 | 97 | 95116 | 47 | 98649 | 97 | 99702 |
| 48 | 86113 | 98 | 95230 | 48 | 98686 | 98 | 99712 |
| 49 | 86378 | 99 | 95341 | 49 | 98723 | 99 | 99721 |
| 1.50 | 0.86639 | 2.00 | 0.95450 | 2.50 | 0.98758 | 3.00 | 0.99730 |
| 51 | 86696 | 01 | 95557 | 51 | 98793 | 01 | 99739 |
| 52 | 87149 | 02 | 95662 | 52 | 98826 | 02 | 99747 |
| 53 | 87398 | 03 | 95764 | 53 | 98859 | 03 | 99755 |
| 54 | 87644 | 04 | 95865 | 54 | 98891 | 04 | 99763 |
| 55 | 87886 | 05 | 95964 | 55 | 98923 | 05 | 99771 |
| 56 | 88124 | 06 | 96060 | 56 | 98953 | 06 | 99779 |
| 57 | 88358 | 07 | 96155 | 57 | 98983 | 07 | 99786 |
| 58 | 88589 | 08 | 96247 | 58 | 99012 | 08 | 99793 |
| 59 | 88817 | 09 | 96338 | 59 | 99040 | 09 | 99800 |
| 1.60 | 0.89040 | 2.10 | 0.96427 | 2.60 | 0.99068 | 3.10 | 0.99806 |
| 61 | 89260 | 11 | 96514 | 61 | 99095 | 11 | 99813 |
| 62 | 89477 | 12 | 96599 | 62 | 99121 | 12 | 99819 |
| 63 | 89690 | 13 | 96683 | 63 | 99146 | 13 | 99825 |
| 64 | 89899 | 14 | 96765 | 64 | 99171 | 14 | 99831 |
| 65 | 90106 | 15 | 96844 | 65 | 99195 | 15 | 99837 |
| 66 | 90309 | 16 | 96923 | 66 | 99219 | 16 | 99842 |
| 67 | 90508 | 17 | 96999 | 67 | 99241 | 17 | 99848 |
| 68 | 90704 | 18 | 97074 | 68 | 99263 | 18 | 99853 |
| 69 | 90897 | 19 | 97148 | 69 | 99285 | 19 | 99858 |

**Appendix IV (Continued)**

| $t$ | $F(t)$ | $t$ | $F(t)$ | $t$ | $F(t)$ | $t$ | $F(t)$ |
|---|---|---|---|---|---|---|---|
| 3.20 | 0.99863 | 3.40 | 0.99933 | 3.60 | 0.99968 | 3.80 | 0.99986 |
| 21 | 99867 | 41 | 99935 | 61 | 99969 | 81 | 99986 |
| 22 | 99872 | 42 | 99937 | 62 | 99971 | 82 | 99987 |
| 23 | 99876 | 43 | 99940 | 63 | 99972 | 83 | 99987 |
| 24 | 99880 | 44 | 99942 | 64 | 99973 | 84 | 99988 |
| 25 | 99885 | 45 | 99944 | 65 | 99974 | 85 | 99988 |
| 26 | 99889 | 46 | 99946 | 66 | 99975 | 86 | 99989 |
| 27 | 99892 | 47 | 99948 | 67 | 99976 | 87 | 99989 |
| 28 | 99896 | 48 | 99950 | 68 | 99977 | 88 | 99990 |
| 29 | 99900 | 49 | 99952 | 69 | 99978 | 89 | 99990 |
| 3.30 | 0.99903 | 3.50 | 0.99953 | 3.70 | 0.99978 | 3.90 | 0.99990 |
| 31 | 99907 | 51 | 99955 | 71 | 99979 | 91 | 99991 |
| 32 | 99910 | 52 | 99957 | 72 | 99980 | 92 | 99991 |
| 33 | 99913 | 53 | 99958 | 73 | 99981 | 93 | 99992 |
| 34 | 99916 | 54 | 99960 | 74 | 99982 | 94 | 99992 |
| 35 | 99919 | 55 | 99961 | 75 | 99982 | 95 | 99992 |
| 36 | 99922 | 56 | 99963 | 76 | 99983 | 96 | 99992 |
| 37 | 99925 | 57 | 99964 | 77 | 99984 | 97 | 99993 |
| 38 | 99928 | 58 | 99966 | 78 | 99984 | 98 | 99993 |
| 39 | 99930 | 59 | 99967 | 79 | 99985 | 99 | 99993 |

# INDEX